Japanese export art in black and gold
1650-1800

Rijksmuseum Amsterdam
Waanders Publishers, Zwolle

Cover: Cat. D.1.1
Frontispiece: Cat. B.13.1 (detail)

Book design: Curve grafische vormgeving, Haarlem
Lithography: LNS, Heemstede
Printing: Waanders Drukkers, Zwolle

©1998 Rijksmuseum Amsterdam
and Uitgeverij Waanders b.v., Zwolle

Catalogue of the exhibition
'Sawasa - Japanese Export Art In Black And Gold 1650 - 1800'
Rijksmuseum Amsterdam,
November 28, 1998 - February 28, 1999.

ISBN 90 400 9279 6
NUGI 926, 911

Preface

The Rijksmuseum is proud to be able to give for the first time a comprehensive view of Sawasa wares. The term Sawasa was chosen to define a particular group of black lacquered and gilt artefacts, produced initially in Japan and later perhaps also in China and Indochina. These wares are characterised by their often European shapes and a peculiar mixture of Asian and European decorative motives and techniques.

In the exhibition attention is focussed on the period from the end of the seventeenth to the end of the eighteenth centuries during which a powerful elite emerged in Batavia (now Jakarta) the Indonesian capital of the Dutch East India Company VOC. This Eurasian group of merchants and administrators was able to use the Asian trade network and the artisan contacts of the VOC to create a singular material culture.

The opportunity to bring the present collection together was created by the generous help of a group of private collectors and institutions. We owe a particular debt of gratitude for their willingness to lend objects to the exhibition to Andrew Lumley, Henk Visser, Ebeltje Hartkamp-Jonxis, Peter Hawkins and Ivon Leijssens. Claude Blair also gave us the benefit of his research files, brought together over the past thirty five years.

Many museums and their staff have been unfailingly helpful with research and loans, we would like to mention StÈphane Vandenberghe and the Gruuthuse Museum, Brugge, Belgium Jan Piet Puijpe and the Legermuseum Delft, Netherlands, Jutta Bäumel and the Staatliche Kunstsammlungen, Rüstkammer, Dresden, Germany, Christiaan Jörg and the Groninger Museum, Groningen, Netherlands, Ken Vos and the Rijksmuseum van Volkenkunde, Leiden, Netherlands, Monika Kopplin and the Museum für Lackkunst, Münster, Germany, Barbara Ford, Stuart Pyrrh and The Metropolitan Museum of Art, New York, U.S.A., Karina Corrigan and the Peabody Essex Museum, Salem U.S.A. and the Victoria and Albert Museum, London, U.K.

We are greatly indebted for research suggestions, archive finds and help to W.E. Bouman, Amsterdam Professor C.L. Davidson, Amsterdam, Jan van Campen, Leiden, Penelope Maskell, London, Nick Norman, Edinburgh, Anthony North, London, Jhr D.J.A. van Lawick van Pabst, Blaricum, Ernst Jochen Schmidt, Jakarta, Willem Terlouw, Leeuwarden, B. van Daalen, Utrecht, Cynthia Viallé, Leiden, Jan van der Waals, Amsterdam, Martine Wolff, Amsterdam, David J. de M Williams, London, Takatoshi Misugi, Kobe, Carolien van Es, Leidschendam and S. M. Voskuil-Groenewegen, The Hague. Femke Koens, Otto de Rijk, Menno Fitski , Ebeltje Hartkamp-Jonxis and Hilda Tomasouw in the Rijksmuseum gave continuous support and practical help. Max de Bruijn co-ordinated research an edited important parts of this catalogue. Peter Hallebeek of the Netherlands Institute for Cultural Heritage did the scientific analysis of the Sawasa objects and wrote a report on his research. Paul Craddock of the Department of Science of the British Museum kindly wrote a contribution about the wider historical context of Sawasa.

Unless otherwise stated, the photographs in this publication were made by David Williams, London, Martin Spillane, London, Bas Martens and Guus de Vries, Histopress Arnhem, Henk Bekker, Madeleine ter Kuile, Margarete Svensson, Fotodienst Rijksmuseum Amsterdam. The design of this catalogue was in the hands of Emiel Hoving, Curve, Haarlem.

This entire project would have been impossible without the participation of an enthusiastic group of trainees who took an important part in research, editing of the catalogue and arranging the exhibition. We owe thanks to Katja Lahaye, Helen Watson, Rosalind Grimmitt, Reni Krijgsman, Quinten Lange, Jolande Roest, Olivier Oosterbaan and Sanne Meijer.

The exhibition has been assembled by Bas Kist, curator of the Department of History, who, with this exhibition and this catalogue, is taking leave of the Rijksmuseum after a career of nearly thirty-five years.

Contents

Introduction

The word Sawasa is used here to indicate a range of precious artefacts such as hilts of hangers and other swords, tobacco- and snuffboxes, cutlery, jewellery, mounts and buttons. The word has a Dutch as well as a Japanese origin. Dutch merchants ordered and purchased Sawasa artefacts from their Nagasaki establishment in Japan from the end of the seventeenth century, using many different spellings of the word such as *sowaas, savas, souassa* and *suassa*. They used the word for objects made of copper alloy with a black and gold surface treatment, a combination of black lacquer and fire gilding. As for the Japanese provenance of the word, this refers to the black surface of the objects only. It is derived from the verb *sawasu*, which means 'applying a thin coat of black lacquer so as to prevent the surface from becoming shiny'. When we use the term Sawasa, we refer both to the alloy and their decorated surface.

The word Sawasa, still in many variations, was used in the Dutch trading area in Asia throughout the eighteenth century. According to written sources, in the early eighteenth century Sawasa wares were produced simultaneously in Japan and in Tonkin (now Vietnam). Late eighteenth century Sawasa was also produced in Batavia (now Jakarta), then the capital of the Dutch commercial empire, and possibly also in Chinese ports, such as Canton. In the eighteenth century, Sawasa was well known in the Dutch Asian settlements. Sawasa artefacts were commonly used and appreciated as jewellery by a small elite. Sawasa wares were acquired as private trade and appear only a few times in official VOC (Dutch East India Company)-records.

Somehow the word never became common in Europe. Instead, collectors of curiosities in the eighteenth and early nineteenth centuries used 'Tonkinese' or 'black chiseled and worked Tonkinese' metalwork or 'beautifully worked Japanese composition' for the same type of objects. Sawasa objects were brought to Europe as presents, curiosities or in jewellery among inheritances. In Europe most of them were however regarded as too rare or valuable to be commonly used. We find Sawasa wares in the most famous eighteenth and early nineteenth century collections of curiosities. Appreciation for the objects declined in the nineteenth century, reference to Tonkinese provenance dissappeared from written sources and the knowledge of the former great value of the objects was lost. Fortunately in the present century a new interest for Asian curiosities emerged. Collectors noted resemblance between various kinds of black and gold objects. Looking for their origins, Rudolf Cederström was the first one to make a link with Japan.[1] The strong black and gilt surface of the objects resembled surface treatment of Japanese sword mounts, especially *tsuba*. In European collections similar artefacts were found, most of them swords which were thought to be of Japanese manufacture. This led Claude Blair to suggest that the black lacquered objects were made of the patinated copper-gold alloy which the Japanese called *shakudô*.[2] As a result, objects with similar decoration were often called *shakudô*.[3] Later the Japanese provenance was confirmed by a dated inscription on a saucer in the Metropolitan Museum of Art in New York, made using the same technique (see Cat. D.4.2).

Recently the Rijksmuseum Amsterdam, working together with private collectors and colleagues in Great Britain, the United States and Holland, planned an exhibition of Sawasa wares. Objects were selected for their appearance with gilded and raised decoration against a black shiny surface. In that stage of research, we did not know better than to name these objects *shakudô/suassa*. Once a large collection was brought together for the first time, objects of this kind could more extensively be studied and compared. Research of materials, techniques and decoration could be combined with a quest for historical source material. This has resulted in a first proposal to call these wares *sawasa* instead of *shakudô*. Our efforts leave us with a number of questions. Some of them we can solve, most of them not. And so we hope this catalogue may serve as a base for further study.

M. de B. & B.K.

Figure 1
Black patinated figure of
Ptah, inlaid with gold,
containing 2.7% of gold,
0.45% of silver and 0.57% of
arsenic in the bronze alloy.
Height 9 cm, EA 27363.

Hympty Km - Corinthium Aes - Wu Tong:
Ancestors and contemporaries of shakudô and sawasa

Paul T. Craddock

Department of Scientific Research, The British Museum, London

Patinated bronzes in the ancient world

The original appearance of ancient bronzes has long been debated by scholars and collectors, in particular whether the surfaces were kept in a highly polished state or were patinated.[1] A good example of this is provided by the ongoing debate as to whether the black patina found on many ancient Chinese mirrors is the result of deliberate patination[2] or just the natural corrosion of a high tin bronze[3] possibly resulting from burial in a waterlogged environment.[4] Similar arguments have been made over the original appearance of silver in Classical Greece, especially where the silver was part gilded. Vickers[5], has suggested that the silver was deliberately blackened to highlight more effectively the gilded figures, in much the same way that the Japanese patinated irogane copper alloys set off their golden inlays.[6]

Overall, the consensus opinion through the last century seems to be that in general bronzes in both Orient and Occident were kept in a polished, metallic state. There is, however, one exception – the black-patinated copper alloys containing small amounts of precious metals and inlaid with precious metals, the Japanese *shakudô* alloys being the most recent and familiar of these. These most subtle and sophisticated of the decorative metals have a long history over a wide cultural area- much longer and much wider than was believed until very recently.[7] This quintessentially Japanese material in fact first appears at the end of the third millennium BC in the Middle East[8] and was made by succeeding cultures, always as a high prestige material that could only be appreciated by the true connoisseur.

Black bronze in the ancient Occident

The earliest extant pieces presently known are Egyptian and include the statue of Amenemhat III (1843-1798 BC), now in the Ortiz collection and a statuette of the crocodile god Sobek, dated to the 19th century BC, now in the Staatlichen Ägyptische Kunst Sammlung in Munich, AS 6080.[9] Analysis showed the body metal of the pieces to be of bronze with small quantities of gold, silver and arsenic and the black patina to contain the copper oxide, cuprite, Cu_2O, identical to the later oriental *shakudô* and Sawasa metals. Giumlia Mair and Quirke[10] believe the technique originated elsewhere in the Middle East and quote the well known scimitar from Bālata-Sichem, in Palestine, now in the Ägyptische Sammlung, Munich, as an early example found outside Egypt[11]. The scimitar may be dated to the 19th century BC by comparison with other examples from Mesopotamia. The technique certainly became well established in Egypt from the 18th Dynasty on as attested by many surviving examples (Fig. 1) and ancient textual references to *hsmn km* (black copper) or *hympty km* (black bronze). Cooney[12] was the first to link the bronzes to the references and pointed out that the black bronzes were always described as inlaid and associated with prestige metalwork, mainly for royal or temple usage.

From the mid second millennium BC the distinctive metal was being used by the Mycenaeans. In another prescient article, Cooney[13] argued that the precious metal inlays set into black panels on the sides of the famous bronze daggers excavated from the Shaft Graves at Mycene and elsewhere were identical with the *hsmn km* he had been studying from Egypt. He believed that the black surface had been produced by treatment with sulphur-containing compounds, thereby creating black copper sulphide, chalcocite, CuS. In fact, recent scientific

study of the daggers and similar pieces in the National Archaeological Museum in Athens[14] has conclusively shown that the black surface has no sulphur, but does contain copper oxide, cuprite, Cu_2O, and the copper alloy panel is of bronze containing small quantities of gold, silver and arsenic, once again identical to the Japanese *shakudô*. The Mycenaean name for the metal was probably *kuwano*, which is likely to have been derived from the Hittite word *kuwano* or *kunna*[15]. The Mycenaean kuwano in turn became the Greek kyanos. This is the word used, for example, by Homer in the *Iliad* to describe the inlay on the silver table belonging to Nestor, and elsewhere the term is clearly a blue-black material.

The metal continued in use through the centuries in Greece and the Middle East and was known to the Roman world as *corinthium aes* (Fig. 2), almost certainly because it was made in that city. Pausanias in his travel guide to Greece[16], compiled in the second

century AD, gives the first description of these patinated metals, stating that the Corinthian bronze was made red hot and dyed (*bapto*) by being plunged into the waters from the Peirene spring. The highly ornate spring head and fountain still exist in the centre of the excavated remains of old Corinth together with the stone channels leading some 30 metres to the stone troughs in the metal-workers quarter[17], a rare instance of a precise ancient description being verified by excavation. Corinthian bronze is described by Pliny in the *Natural History*[18] and Plutarch in the *Moralia*[19] and from these authors we learn that it was an alloy of copper with small quantities of gold and silver. From these and other sources we can also glean that the metal was both patinated and inlaid[20]. It is perhaps significant that analysis of Roman pieces has revealed not only gold and silver but also enhanced levels of arsenic[21], as has been found in both earlier and later pieces, including

Figure 2. Small Roman plaque, inlaid with gold and silver (the latter now largely missing), containing 0.6% of gold, 1.2% of silver and 1.1% of arsenic in the bronze alloy. GR 1979, 12-13,1.

Figure 3. The earliest known instructions for the preparation of a shakudô-type patinated metal. 15th century Syriac copy of an earlier manuscript based on the Alexandrian alchemist Zosimos, now preserved in the University Library, Cambridge, Syriac manuscript Mm 6.29. Did the secrets of the preparation pass from Occident to the Orient in documents such as this?

Figure 4. A Chinese precursor to shakudô. Bronze tally stick in the form of a tiger, patinated and inlaid. On display in the Xian Museum. Warring States Period (475-321 BC).

shakudô itself [22]. The most detailed description of the manufacture and properties of Corinthian bronze is given, perhaps not surprisingly, by the Alexandrian alchemists to whom processes of patination or *iosis* were of central importance. A 15th century Syriac manuscript now preserved in Cambridge, based on an 11th century Greek version of an original text by Zosimos, who lived in the third century AD, describes how black copper or Corinthian bronze was to be prepared [23] (Fig. 3). This was achieved by treating a copper alloy containing about 6.5% each of gold and silver with a boiling aqueous solution of various salts including vinegar and verdigris (Berthelot mistranslates these as vitriol), recalling the more recent recipes for the manufacture of *shakudô*.

The process seems to have become extinct in the West sometime in the post-Roman period although examples are known from Anglo-Saxon England [24] and also from the Avars of the Carpathians. The Syriac manuscript also shows that as late as the 15th century details of the process were still known in the Middle East, although no Islamic examples have yet been identified.

Black bronzes in the early Orient

For the later history of the material, we have to cross over central Asia to the Orient. At present there is little early artefactual or documentary evidence. Needham [25] considered that the Japanese *shakudô* must have had Chinese precursors and he set about examining the Chinese literature for likely candidates. He came across references to a series of coloured golds that apparently existed in a variety of colours from scarlet *chhih chin* through purple, *tzu chin* to *tzu mo chin*, or purple sheen golds. References to these alloys occur in the Chinese literature from about the 5th century AD, together with statements that they were not indigenous but had come to China from the West. In one Chinese text of 712 AD there is a reference to a seven-fold transformation from yellow through red scarlet purple and finally purple sheen gold, and Needham noted the similarity to the colour transformation of base gold alloys of the Western alchemists, by chemical treatment of their surfaces, progressing from yellow through to the desired purple or *iosis*, which he equated with a *shakudô*-like metal.

However, when other references to

coloured golds in south east Asia are considered it is by no means clear that these Chinese scarlet and purple sheen golds should be interpreted thus. In both the Indian classics, the *Ramayana* and the *Mahabharata* there are references to *jambunada* gold [26] which has been interpreted both as gold coming from the river Jambu, or that it resembled the *jamba*, a red-purple fruit, similar to a damson. Support for the latter view is given by contemporary descriptions that the *jambunada* gold was indeed scarlet. In later centuries, up to the present day, gold of high purity was regularly treated to produce a range of colours from red through purple to blue by treatment with a poultice of tamarind pulp containing nitre, common salt and elemental sulphur. [27] In the absence of other evidence these would seem to be more obvious candidates for *tzu mo chin* than *shakudô*.

However references to metals related etymologically to *tzu mo chin* do occur outside China, notably in Tibet and there the evidence does seem to suggest that we are dealing with a patinated copper alloy containing, amongst other things, precious metals.

Figure 5. *A selection of wu tong ink boxes formerly in the Collier collection, now in the British Museum,* OA 1992, 11-9, 1-6.

Figure 6. *Lids of the wu tong ink boxes, showing a variety of typical designs and calligraphy typical of the early 20th century.*

In particular there was a special alloy, *zi-khyim*, described in Tibetan records from the 10th century AD, that was either found as a natural alloy in the ground, or had to be synthesised. [28] The artificial alloy contained eight materials, copper with gold, silver, white iron, black and white lead (lead and tin?), rock crystal and mercury. This, when cast, was treated with 'poisonous water' (acid?) which gave it a purple-red iridescence.

Accepting that some caution is necessary, *zi-khyim* clearly has parallels with Corinthian bronze and the *shakudô* alloys. It was a copper alloy containing, amongst other things, gold and silver, upon which patination treatments produced an iridescent purple colour.

The origin of the word *zi-khyim* is of some interest. Most Tibetan metallurgical terms are of sanskrit origin, but *zi-khyim* is not. Instead it is of Chinese origin, more specifically it is derived from *ch'ih chin*. [29] Thus if they are the same or related alloys then Needham was indeed correct to associate the *tzu chin*, purple sheen gold with the *iosis* of the Western alchemists and the *shakudô* of the Japanese. However the origin of the name does suggest that the alloy had come to Tibet from China, which might be taken as indicating an independent origin for the oriental patinated bronzes.

Figure 7 . Group of dark patinated alloy and silver pipe stems. The top three are of wu tong, the lowest is of red copper, alloyed with arsenic replacing the gold and silver in the alloy. OA 1996, 1-15, 1-5.

Wu tong

As yet no suitably patinated *shakudô*-type alloys have been identified from early China, although it would be interesting to be able to analyse the tiger-shaped tally stick of lustrous purple-black bronze inlaid with gold calligraphy, dated to the Warring States period, that is now on display in the Xian Museum in China (Fig. 4) (I am grateful to G. Weisgerber for bringing this piece to my attention). Kerr[30] notes 17th century Chinese reports of vessels purported to have been cast from an alloy of copper, gold and silver that had come about when a temple burnt down and the ritual vessels of the three metals melted and co-mingled. Similar

apocryphal stories were told of the origins of *corinthium aes* 1500 years before.

In later centuries such alloys were made in Yunnan in the south-west of China, which is, perhaps significantly, adjacent to Tibet. These are the *wu chin* or *wu tong* metals (Figs. 5 & 6). [31] They were first noted by Collier[32], a Canadian biochemist teaching in Sichuan and Yunnan in the 1930's who made a collection of *wu tong* that has subsequently been donated to the university of Alberta in Edmonton, with the exception of the pieces shown in Fig. 5. The alloy is usually of copper containing about a percent each of gold and silver, this is inlaid with silver, polished and patinated.

In the 19th and early 20th centuries production concentrated on items such as small vessels and containers and the stems of tobacco pipes (Fig. 7). Small boxes for carrying opium and ink boxes were especially common, the latter often being given as presents to reward success in the Civil Service examinations (Figs. 5 & 6). Although the basic components of *wu tong* are the same as *shakudô* and *Sawasa*, there are significant differences in

construction and inlay techniques [33]. A metallographic examination of a section through the metal revealed it to be a composite. A thin sheet of the alloy containing the precious metal was braised with silver solder (containing about 50% of silver, 40% of copper, 4% of zinc and 1% of lead) to a thicker sheet of red brass (copper containing about 5% of zinc). This composite was then rolled down to a thickness of about 0.4 mm, made up of about 0.3 mm of brass and 0.1 mm of wu tong. The design or inscription was engraved into the surface of the wu tong, and then inlaid with wires of the silver solder. The piece was heated to just above 820°C, causing the silver solder to melt into the groove (Fig. 8) and after cooling the whole surface was polished flat. The sheets were then ready to be used in the construction of the boxes and other artefacts. Usually the object was constructed of copper sheet

to which the wu tong composite was soldered. The construction can be exemplified by the oval box illustrated in Fig. 9. The box comprises a base and sides with a rim or lip all of copper. The wu tong composite was soldered to the sides. The lid is a sheet with side walls to both of which the wu tong composite was soldered. Raised strips of silver were added at the edges to conceal the soldered joins on the outside, and to protect the wu tong surfaces.

The final stage was patination. It is still not certain how this was achieved. It is claimed both in old information sheets on the process [34] and by the current operatives at the Kunming Arts and Craft Mill (see below) that the patination was achieved by repeated handling, the ammonium and sodium salts in the average sweaty palm being sufficient to produce the black patina over the course of several hours. Recent experiments by

Giumlia Mair and Lehr [35] showed the method worked, but this still seems an inherently unlikely method for a regular production process. Mang Zidan and Han Rubin [36] experimented with tea water and with mixtures of organic acids (acetic, lactic and tannic). They obtained a good black patina except that X-ray diffraction showed that it contained principally silver oxide with only a little copper oxide whereas the original contains only copper oxide.

Alongside the true wu tong there was also a cheaper version, known as hong tong, red copper, which had a deep chocolate brown patina. Analysis of an example purchased in Kunming, and now in the British Museum (Fig. 7), showed the metal to contain a few percent of arsenic rather than precious metal.

The making of wu tong is very much an indigenous craft of Yunnan and there is nothing to suggest either outside origin and contacts, or of a history stretching back into antiquity. Indeed the material is little known not just outside of China, but even outside of Yunnan itself. Production seems to have been restricted to one centre in the village of Yuejiawan near to the town of Shiping on Lake Yinlong (Fig. 10), about 200 km south of Kunming, the provincial capital of Yunnan. Local records and legends state that production was started by two brothers of the Yue family which had then just arrived in the area in the mid 17th century. The family business thrived through succeeding generations, and their position as leading manufacturers recalls the Goto family of shakudô makers in Japan. However, the turmoil in China in this century proved disastrous for the rather esoteric luxury item. Production continued at Yuejiawan through the early years of the Republic, with Su Jincheng as the last master craftsman, until the civil war and the Japanese invasion. Then the few remaining craftsmen, including Su Jincheng, moved to Kunming, where

Figure 8. *Cross section through the inlay of silver solder clearly showing it had been melted into place. The dark regions in the inlay are dendrites of the copper-rich phase (83% copper, 10% silver, 6% zinc) which solidified first. The bright speckled regions are the silver-rich copper-silver eutectic (72% silver 24% copper, 3% zinc). Scanning electron micrograph, back scattered electron image. Inlay depth 0.18 mm. M. Wayman/British Museum.*

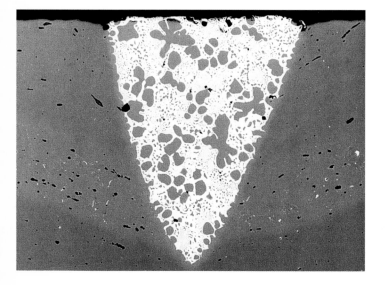

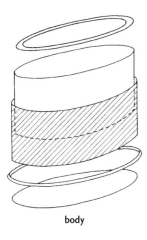

body

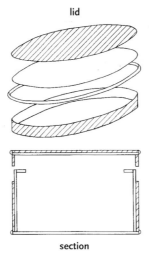

lid

section

Figure 9. *Construction of an oval wu tong box, using the central box in Fig. 4. as an example. Left: exploded view of the body. Right: (above) exploded view of the lid. (below) cross section through the body and lid. The hatched components are of the wu tong composite sheets and carry the inlay, soldered to the underlying thicker support sheets of copper.*
Drawn by B. Craddock.

work continued intermittently before ending in about 1960. Patinated copper alloys are still made and sold in the tourists shops of Kunming including the bright orange variegated or 'spotted' bronzes, apparently produced by treatment with ferric chloride, and copper alloys with an artificial green 'antique' patina. One of the firms producing these patinated bronzes, the Kunming Arts and Craft Mill, also claims to produce *wu tong*, known as 'jet bronze'. However a visit to their workshops showed that although they did indeed have a few pieces of old *wu tong*, they had no recent pieces for sale and were reluctant to accept a commission, suggesting they had not made any for some years.

Shakudô has long been regarded as quintessentially Japanese. The Dutch merchants who brought back the Sawasa wares must have thought they were introducing a new and exotic material into Europe. In fact similar materials had existed in the West thousands of years previously.

The connection between the ancient patinated metals of the Occident and the more recent metals of the Orient is unproven, but the knowledge could have passed from West to East when the rise

of Christianity to the status of the official religion in the Late Roman Empire drove the pagan philosophers and heretic sects such as the Nestorians, to Persia and beyond.

One of the problems with the Japanese *irogane* alloys has been the absence of precursors. Between the

Roman *corinthium aes* and the Japanese *shakudô* there are gaps of at least a millennium and over five thousand kilometres. The early references to apparently similar materials in Tibet and in China, together with the more recent *wu tong*, apparently indigenous to West China, have helped to bridge that gap.

Figure 10. *The village of Yuejiawan on Lake Yinlong, some 200 km south of Kunming, the traditional centre of wu tong production from the 17th to mid-20th centuries.*

Fig. 1. Map of the East-
Indies. W. Blaeu,
Amsterdam 1632-33.
Rijksmuseum Amsterdam,

Sawasa

Max de Bruijn

Bas Kist

Sawasa wares were the product of cultural interaction between Asia and Europe. As a consequence of European expansion to Asia and global trade in the seventeenth century, mutual interest arose in the peculiarities of each other's culture. The Dutch and other Europeans brought rare objects back from their travels, which whetted the taste for exotic rarities in Europe. In the Eurasian trade port of Batavia (now Jakarta) a wealthy governmental and commercial elite emerged which had access to the production centres of these trans-cultural artefacts and the means to acquire them. Sawasa demonstrates not only the intercontinental commercial connections created by the Dutch East India Company (VOC) but also the mutual cultural influences between Europe and Asia. The Sawasa exhibition will position Sawasa wares in the total spectrum of Asian export arts.

The terms Sawasa and shakudô

To prevent any possible confusion, we will discuss here the use of the word *shakudô* in relation to the objects in this catalogue. Objects of this kind have often been named *shakudô*, referring to the traditional Japanese copper-gold alloy used in artefacts, especially sword-furniture. This misconception originated from a combination of facts and a babel-like confusion of terms. Some of our objects have a proven Japanese origin and they resemble Japanese *tsuba* with their black and gold shiny surfaces. As the black surfaces on tsuba are often patinated, this led to the assumption that the black surfaces on 'our' wares were also patinated. The Japanese

Fig. 2. *W.H. Medhurst: 'An English and Japanese and Japanese and English Vocabulary' (Batavia, 1830), p. 73. Royal Institute of Linguistics and Anthropology (KITLV), Leiden.*

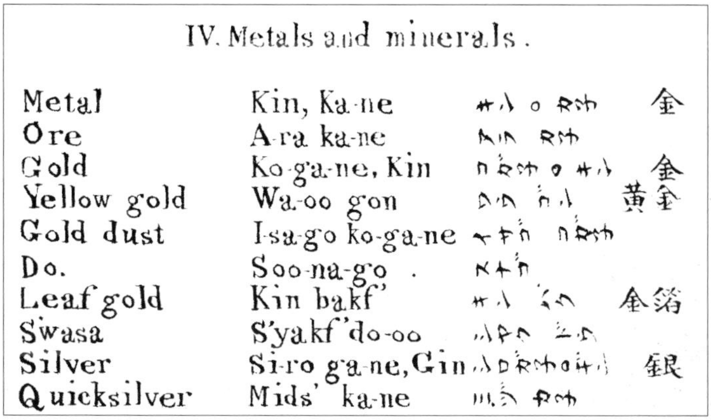

IV. Metals and minerals .

Metal	Kin, Ka-ne	ﻢﻟ o ﺭﺻﻪ	金
Ore	A-ra ka-ne	ﻙﻟﻟ ﺭﺻﻪ	
Gold	Ko-ga-ne, Kin	ﻥ ﺭﺻﻪ o ﻢﻟ	金
Yellow gold	Wa-oo gon	ﻥﻟﻟ ﻩﻟ ﻟ	黄金
Gold dust	I-sa-go ko-ga-ne	ﻙﻑﻥ ﻥ ﺭﺻﻪ	
Do.	Soo-na-go .	ﻙﻑﻥ	
Leaf gold	Kin bakf'	ﻢﻟ ﻵ	金箔
Swasa	S'yakf'do-oo	ﻟﻷﻥ ﻵﻷ	
Silver	Si-ro ga-ne, Gin	ﻷﻩﺭﻣﻩﻟﺠ	銀
Quicksilver	Mids' ka-ne	ﻟﻟﺠ ﺭﺻﻪ	

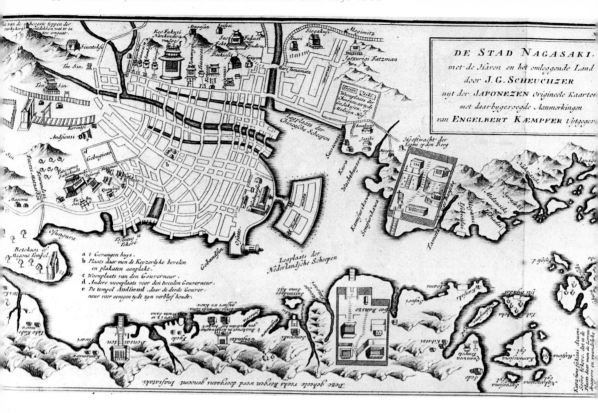

Fig. 4. *Plan of Nagasaki with the Dutch and Chinese trade settlements. E. Kaempfer: Beschrijving van Japan (Amsterdam, 1733), p. 180. Amsterdam University Library, Inv. No. 274 A6-E.*

Fig. 3. *Achinese keris with a black and gold decorated hilt, probably Sawasa. National Museum of Indonesia, Jakarta, Inv. No. E.146 (Bataviaasch Genootschap nr. 7858).*

coloured the copper-gold alloy black by chemically treating the surface, a technique used for several centuries. Further to this, an etymological connection was suggested between *shakudô* and *suassa*, a gold-copper alloy widely used in the Indonesian archipelago. Next followed the assumption that with the words savas, siowaas, or sowaas, seventeenth and eighteenth century European merchants in Asia were referring to shakudô.

We suggest using the word Sawasa from here on when we refer to the objects in this catalogue that are made for the European market and consist of an alloy of copper with gold, silver and arsenic, decorated with black lacquer and gold. Europeans in the seventeenth and eighteenth century never used *shakudô* or similar words for goods they purchased in Japan. They used sowaas, suassa, sawassa, or savas for objects made of this

alloy, originating from either Japan, Tonkin or Indonesia. Only in the early nineteenth century the word 'syaks do-oo' is used as a translation for the word 'swasa' in an English-Japanese vocabulary.[1] The author, W.H. Medhurst, lived in Batavia and never visited Japan. No doubt he picked up the word in Batavia and sought a Japanese equivalent. A Dutch merchant in Japan uses the word 'Shakfdo' for black patinated metal artefacts.[2] Consequently, this term was also applied to Sawasa wares.

The origins of the words sowaas, suassa and other derivations are not entirely clear. As far as Japan is concerned, there is, however, quite a reasonable explanation. The verb *sawasu* means *'covering with a thin layer of black lacquer to prevent from shining'*[3]. This word is pronounced with a silent 'u', explaining the shorter sowaas or sawas the Dutch

generally used in the Malay world for a multitude of gold alloys.[8] Before 1680 the Dutch seemed to have used the words *swasse* or *suwassche* both for Indonesian as well as Japanese objects. In 1644 the King of Achin (north-Sumatra) presented some visiting Dutch merchants from Batavia with *'a Moorish knife, the hilt made of swasse, being a mixture of copper and gold'* and *'a swasse kris'*[9]. These objects seem entirely Indonesian.[10] The *keris* is a typically Indonesian weapon. Also 'Moorish' or Arab influence on arms was quite common in Indonesia, especially in Achin, which was the nearest port coming from the Middle East. Another reference is from 1673 when 'six *suwasche* sword-plates' were ordered from Japan for a governor of Tonkin (North Vietnam).[11] Without any other previous mention of European swords, these were probably *tsuba* of Japanese swords. The confusion can be explained by the fact that the Dutch encountered a widespread use of alloys, decorations and techniques all over Asia. Furthermore, Asian metallurgy was subject to constant change because of inter-Asian trade. Japanese and Chinese lived all over Asia. The Chinese junk trade permanently connected all Asian areas, while Arabs maintained a trade connection with the Far East long before Europeans arrived in Asia.

As for *shakudô*, we use this word here only when we refer to the alloy, e.g. copper containing gold, silver and arsenic. A Sawasa hanger hilt and Japanese sword furniture have certain resemblances, for instance the gold on black effect.[12] However, on closer inspection, the objects not only have a different appearance, they are completely different. With *shakudô*, the black shiny effect is achieved either by chemical patinating or by the use of the natural property of the alloy to turn dark when polished. On Sawasa wares the black surfaces are all lacquered. Strangely enough, most Sawasa wares are made of

a copper alloy containing silver, gold and arsenic, the same alloy the Japanese used for *shakudô*. In the context of this catalogue we therefore decided to retain the word *shakudô*, but only for the alloy in our objects.

Lacquered Sawasa and patinated shakudô

It is interesting to speculate why the Japanese produced a black surface by using lacquer, while at the same time they could get a similar result with patination. One explanation could be that there was a difference in products for export and for the home market. It has been suggested that the Japanese imitated the patination of the *shakudô*-alloy in lacquer.[13] As the black surfaces on Japanese *tsuba* are patinated, the lacquer on Sawasa wares would be the imitation. This also implies a difference in quality. Sawasa wares would then be the imitations, meant for export, while the Japanese made the 'real *shakudô*' for the home market. However, several of our objects with lacquered black surfaces have applied pieces of *shakudô* metal with dark patination.[14] Even more remarkable is that all our objects, except a few, including the ones which are decorated in Chinese taste, are made of the precious *shakudô* metal. If Sawasa wares for export were of low quality, this should also be reflected in the lower quality of their decoration and technique. However, the lacquer on most objects is of high quality and the objects have a very ingenious construction. Nonetheless, the decoration shows an inextricable mixture of Chinese and Japanese influences, often within one object. Apparently different artisans, some of them highly skilled, others less so, worked on the same objects.

The history of Sawasa wares: hilts and tobacco boxes from Japan

Sawasa wares appear in written sources at the end of the seventeenth century,

used.[4] The word sowaas is used for the first time in connection with our artefacts by Engelbert Kaempfer who worked in Japan in the years 1690 to 1692. A tobacco box mentioned in 1695[5] and a transaction concerning sword hilts in 1697[6] clearly mark the Japanese provenance of these artefacts and the word. In the same years a distinction is made in the inventory of a deceased Governor-General in Batavia between two kinds of *'savas'*, one of which is Japanese. This Governor General, Joan van Hoorn (1653-1711), worked in Deshima for a long time and owned a large collection of Japanese artefacts.[7] After this, Sawasa is commonly used in Batavia throughout the eighteenth century, though not any more in direct relation to Japan.

Various other etymological connections with the word Sawasa led to much confusion in Asia. The word suasa was

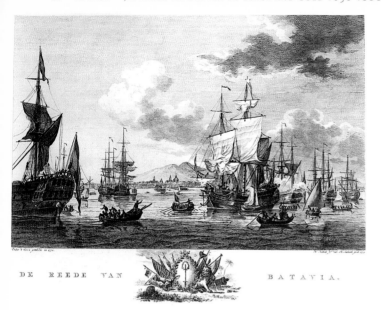

DE   REEDE   VAN   BATAVIA.

Fig. 5. *Batavia roads in 1772. Drawing by H. Kobell, engraved by M. Sallieth. Rijksmuseum Amsterdam, Inv. No. FM 5019.*

ordered from Japan by Dutch merchants from Batavia. The oldest reference is a *'very peculiar copper gilded enamelled Japanese souatsche Tobacco box'*, donated in 1695 by Governor-General Willem van Outhoorn to his relative Dirck Graswinckel in Holland. With the box went a pipe case *'skilfully plated on both sides with massive gold filigree'*.[15] The description is made by Graswinckel himself who never went to Asia but who belonged to a family traditionally involved in the Asian trade. His description shows both the novelty of the *'souatsch'* object as well as the confusion about what it is. Graswinckel clearly did not know exactly what he owned. From his description however we can deduce a little what he saw: a box made of copper, decorated in gold and with a sort of coating described as enamel.[16]

In approximately the same period, Dutch merchants in Asia were involved in the production of Sawasa hanger hilts in Japan. Cornelis van Outhoorn, *opperhoofd* or director of the VOC trading station of Deshima, in the harbour of Nagasaki, reported in October 1696 by

letter to Governor-General and Council in Batavia: *'the requested [ ] 3 suasse hanger hilts have been sent by the [ship] Jerusalem'*[17] costing 34 taels together. *Tael* or *tayl* was an Asian standard for coins and precious metals, worth at that time about three-and-a-half guilders.[18] The Journal of Deshima in the same month added that the *'sawasse'* hilts were gilded and sent with *'their 3 lacquered ray-skin scabbards'*.[19] Having already used two different words for the same wares a Dutch clerk added a third, *'siowasse'* in the same month when the new *opperhoofd* Hendrik Dijckman again reported to Batavia the sending of the hilts mentioned earlier.[20] Little more about this kind of transaction was revealed until almost a year later the VOC-ship 'Carthago' arrived in Deshima with *'6 gilt hangerblades to be fitted here with scabbards and mounts'*, the same ship leaving on November 3 with *'6 savatse hanger hilts with their scabbards'*.[21] Opperhoofd Dijckman also referred to the objects in a letter to Batavia accompanying the shipload. He or his clerk again used another spelling for

Sawasa: *'the 6 souasse hangerhilts and 6 ditto tobacco boxes'*[22].

In this transaction, the Dutch merchants were dealing with something rather new. They described quite accurately the process of trade of a few objects only, of little value compared to the price of a bulk shipload. The Japanese had something special for sale, which the Dutch did not have in Batavia and which, could only be manufactured in or around Deshima. It was normal for Dutchmen in Asia to ship blades and hilts separately. Important people had their swords furbished according to their personal status. The swords had to be impressive and expensive. Dutch merchants in Batavia ordered the decorated blades from famous craftsmen in Europe. For the hilt, they chose something special in accordance to the latest local fashion. This was what the Japanese could provide. They could produce special hilts made of *savats, siowassa, souasse* or *suasse*. These hilts were quite expensive, one hilt almost the equivalent of a month's wages of an *onderkoopman*, a low ranking merchant. Interestingly enough, the Dutch merchants in Asia, unlike Graswinckel in Europe, did seem to know what kind of material Sawasa wares were made of.

Apart from hilts, the Japanese could deliver another speciality: scabbards made of lacquered fish skins, such as ray skin and shark skin. The Dutch made huge profits with the import of ray skins or *rochevellen* into Japan, which they got from Siam (now Thailand), Cambodia and Tonkin (North Vietnam). The Japanese partly bought them as raw materials for their own use[23] and as seems the case with our scabbards converted them to high quality products for export. The Japanese were well known for their skills in improving the appearance of ray skin. *Opperhoofd* of Deshima Andreas Cleyer, noted his admiration in the daily Journal kept at Deshima in 1682: *'the ray skins [ ] were sent to the city for cleaning, which the Japanese did with great skill. [ ] They do this often: treating things which at first seem worthless and now look perfect'* [24].

An 'artificial metal' composed of copper, silver and gold, decorated with gilt flowers

Unofficial contemporary sources explain more about the material of the 1695 tobacco box and the 1697 Japanese hilts and boxes. Adding another version of the word, the German Engelbert Kaempfer gave a definition of *'sowaas'*. Kaempfer served the Dutch East India Company as a doctor of medicine. In his famous *History and Description of Japan*, based on his experience when working in Deshima in the years 1690 to 1692, he listed goods exported from Japan by the Dutch, including: *'[ ] hard skins of fishes, which they work with uncommon neatness and*

dexterity, stone, copper, gold and Sowaas. (The latter is an artificial metal composed of copper, silver and gold, and esteemed equal in value to silver, if not superior.)' [25]. From another description of *sowaas* by Kaempfer, we learn that although the metal was used elsewhere in Asia, the Japanese were the most skilled in converting it into artefacts. Kaempfer also revealed something about the appearance of the metal: it is blackish but it resembles gold when worked by an artisan: *'No Eastern nation is that skilled and able in working, sculpting, cutting and gilding of Sowaas, which is a special kind of precious blackish metal, artificially made of copper with some gold. Objects made of this metal are like gold when they come from the hands of the artisan, and are really only slightly less in colour and beauty than gold.'* [26] Kaempfer explained that in Nagasaki wares of this metal were made exclusively for the foreign market. He also claimed handicrafts from Nagasaki

usually were of lower quality than handicrafts from elsewhere in Japan: *'Handicrafts from Nagasaki usually are not that good as those from other parts of the Empire, though everything is sold more expensively, especially to the Foreigners. However, those things worked in Gold, Silver and Sawaas, being wares which are more suitable for Foreign than for Domestic Trade, are much better here and of finer and more beautiful art, then I believe is made anywhere else.'* [27]

His equally famous German contemporary Georg Eberhard Rumphius (1628-1702), who lived most of his life on Amboina, also knew about the metal, naming it *'black suassa'*, although he did not know the exact composition of the alloy: *'Black suassa comes from Tonquin and Japon being a kind of red copper which is always black on the outside, but colours copperwise when polished, the alloy of which I do not know; it is commonly used*

Fig. 7. Frontispiece from: E. Kaempfer: Beschrijving van Japan (Amsterdam, 1733), p. 180. Amsterdam University Library, Inv. No. 274 A6-E.

Fig. 8. Frontispiece from: G.E. Rumphius, 'De Amboinsche Rariteit Kamer' (Amsterdam, 1741) Rijksmuseum Amsterdam, Inv. No. 306A11.

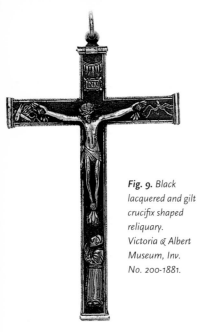

Fig. 9. *Black lacquered and gilt crucifix shaped reliquary. Victoria & Albert Museum, Inv. No. 200-1881.*

for sword hilts, mountings on canes and coat buttons, which are inlaid or gilt with gold flowers'[28]. Rumphius noted that *suassa*, as an alloy, was highly regarded by all Asian nations. Even the Portuguese, he states, fancied it. This

may explain two crucifixes in the Victoria & Albert Museum, made of *shakudô* metal, lacquered and decorated with gilded ornaments.[29] Rumphius says there are two kinds of *suassa* in Asia: a natural and an artificial alloy. From European literature, Rumphius could not explain the use of the alloy. Therefore, he described the use of it from his own experience in Indonesia, where people preferred it to gold.

Rumphius, who wrote between 1660 and 1699 and never visited Japan, is the only one who tells us something about the outward appearance of Sawasa wares. Thanks to him, it is now possible to match some written descriptions with existing objects. In the same period as the 1697 hilt transaction, Czar Peter the Great (1672-1725) donated a small group of objects, part of a larger collection of gifts, to August II Elector of Saxony at the court of Dresden. As a regular visitor to Holland and importer of Dutch technology into Russia, Peter may well have acquired them in Holland. The

objects are a hanger, a small-sword and a cane *'said to be of Japanese manufacture'*[30]. The swords have European blades. The hilts, cane handle and fittings on the scabbards are made of a copper-alloy decorated in black with gilded flowers and figures. The scabbard of the small-sword and the cane are covered with polished and lacquered shark skin, the other scabbard with the similarly treated ray skin. This use of fish skins we recognise from the descriptions by Kaempfer and Cleyer. Another sword fits in the same period. It is a hanger with similar appearance, presented around 1700 by the VOC to Johannes van Leenen (1643-1721) in honour of his services.[31] The costly etched and gilt blade is almost certainly Dutch. The hilt shows gilt flowers in relief designs and with the sword belongs a scabbard, covered with shark skin. Analysis shows that this hilt and similar hilts consist of the then expensive gold-silver-copper alloy, as mentioned by Kaempfer. A document on parchment, written by an eighteenth century descendant of Van Leenen, confirms the Japanese provenance of the hanger.

Dated somewhat later, several objects confirm the link between alloy and decoration. A saucer in the Metropolitan Museum of Art in New York marked and dated 'IAPAN·ANNO·1731' displays

Fig. 11. *Three hangers with French blades, made c. 1700. The Sawasa hilts have presumably been fitted in Japan. One (Z.O.2815) has a distinctly European mythological scene on the outside of the shell guard. The Hermitage Museum, St. Petersburg, Inv. Nos. z.o. 2815, z.o.1344 en z.o.1374.*

Fig. 12a. Silver tobacco box with the initials of Hendrik Thomson, chief surgeon in Deshima 1730. Rijksmuseum Amsterdam, Inv. No. NG-313.

Fig. 12. Still life with Sawasa cups and saucers by Pieter G. van Roestraten (1627-1700). Private property. Picture from: Luttervelt, R. van, 'Kunst in Nederland. Schilders van het stilleven' (Naarden, 1947), plate 30.

gilded flower decoration and is made of the alloy mentioned by Kaempfer.[32] The saucer forms a pair with a cup executed in the same way. A tobacco box of similar appearance, though made of silver, proves that this kind of decoration was used commonly by Japanese craftsmen in Nagasaki on European-style objects. According to the inscription, Hendrik Thomson, chief surgeon at Deshima, owned the box in 1730.[33] Just before 1700, pairs of cups and saucers with similar decoration were depicted on a still life by Pieter Gerritszoon van Roestraten (1627-1700).[34]

Quality lacquer on metal objects

A striking feature of the Sawasa wares is the thin layer of strong black or brown lacquer. On most objects, it has survived the ages almost without a scratch. Analysis shows that heating has hardened the lacquer, whereas on wooden surfaces, lacquer was dried in the open air. We have not been able to establish the exact provenance of Sawasa wares from the lacquer. The raw lacquer, Dutch merchants called it *namrack*, was the exudate of three similar but different trees growing in several Asian countries. The Japanese have always preferred the *Rhus Vernicifera*, which gives the best quality lacquer. However, they also used lesser quality *namrack*, which was imported in huge quantities from China and Indochina by the Dutch and the Chinese. Because of its high quality, one would expect the lacquer on the wares in this catalogue to be of the *Rhus Vernicifera*, but we have not found evidence for this yet.

Descriptions of the qualities of Asian lacquer appear in European literature from the end of the seventeenth century. Attention has mostly been focussed on the use of lacquer on wooden surfaces. Sources are very rare about the use on

Fig. 12b. Inscription 'IAPAN·ANNO·1731' on the back of a Sawasa saucer, catalogue D.4.2. Metropolitan Museum, New York, Inv. No. 1984.233b.

metal surfaces. In 1720, the Italian Jesuit Bonanni published a work about *'Chinese varnish'*, partly based on knowledge of other Jesuits such as Le Comte, Du Halde and d'Incarville.[35] In the course of the eighteenth century, it was translated many times in several European languages. This coincided with the European fashion for imitation Asian lacquerwork.

Bonanni used *'Chinese varnish'* for lacquers used in different Asian countries: *'Chinese varnish [ ] is used in China and also in Tonquin and the large island of Japan'*. He noted the Japanese used it for furniture and also on swords.[36] He described a salesman in

Rome who sold metal drinking utensils with a layer of strong Asian lacquer, which could withstand high temperatures. He probably referred to the large urns such as depicted in this catalogue (category D):

'Some years ago a stranger came to Rome who had several varnished works for sale, all made of copper, most of them chocolate and coffee utensils. To prove it was the real Chinese varnish, he put it [the utensils] on burning coal where they remained undamaged [ ] one could also make coffee in these varnished vessels [ ] without the heat damaging the varnish.'[37]

Elsewhere in his book, he described decoration used on Chinese export wares, with lacquer and gold decoration in relief designs. With China, he again seemed to mean the whole of Asia:

'Among the works brought from China to Europe, there are few which are not decorated with some gold figures, or foliage,

though this usually lays bare most of the varnish [ ] If one wants to copy these decoration, one should note that on most of these works these kinds of ornaments are in relief [ ] relief works such as arabesques to ones own choice, namely trees, plants, birds, chapels and the such: which are made of golddust.'[38]

Sawasa in private and illicit trade

After the 1697 sword transaction, Sawasa wares disappear from official records. This implies that they were confined to private or illicit trade. The Japanese allowed the Dutch in Deshima private purchases amounting to 40,000 taels.[39] This so-called Kambang trade was listed in the Deshima records yet it was seldom specified. Records regularly mentioned curiosities, under which Sawasa wares such as tobacco boxes may have been listed. Kaempfer wrote about this private trade: 'After the [official] sale, some Wares

of the Country are auctioned, such as lacquered work, several objects made of copper, which the Japanese work with extreme dexterity, and some other goods [this happens] in a separate place, built for this purpose'[40]. The Japanese prohibited the trade in certain goods. When caught smuggling, Dutch merchants would be expelled from the country. Japanese smugglers usually were beheaded, sometimes even on Deshima to discourage the Dutch from smuggling.[41]
In Kaempfers time it was illegal to export 'metals with Japanese marks' from Japan.[42] This may explain why none of the Sawasa wares are signed.

Another possibility of trade in Sawasa wares from Nagasaki to Batavia, lies in the Chinese junk trade. The Chinese had a large settlement in Nagasaki. Like the Dutch, they were confined to a restricted area. Chinese trade tripled the amount of goods transported in and out Japan by the Dutch. In fact, the Dutch, following the Portuguese example, participated in the Chinese trade triangle China-Batavia-Manilla. In those days Batavia was a Chinese port as much as the Asian capital of the Dutch commercial empire. The inter-Asian trade of the VOC always had an important Chinese component. Illicit and private trade by Dutch and Chinese may well have been responsible for the amounts of Sawasa wares in Batavia.

Illegal arms

Strictly speaking, Sawasa sword furniture was an illegal export. Since the late 16th century, Japan had developed an intensive weapons trade, first with the Portuguese, later with the English and the Dutch. The Japanese were mainly interested in European firearms. On the other hand, Europeans purchased Japanese weapons primarily as curiosities. The Dutch painter Rembrandt van Rijn (1606-1669), for instance, owned a Japanese sword. In Kaempfer's time,

Fig. 13. *Japanese screen with a Dutch East Indiaman and a Chinese junk, early 18th century. Rijksmuseum Amsterdam, Inv. No. NG-696.*

Fig. 14. Dumb waiter, composed from Chinese porcelain and Japanese Imari ware, decorated with the crests of the Van Brederode and Van Buren families, early 18th century. Rijksmuseum Amsterdam, Inv. No. BK-BR-541.

Batavia

Confined to private trade, we only find references to Japanese Sawasa wares in private papers such as inventories of rich households in Batavia from the beginning of the eighteenth century. For instance the inventories made after the deaths of the Governors-General Joan van Hoorn (1653-1711) and Gustaaf Willem Baron van Imhoff (1705-1750) mention quantities of *'savas'*, used as a noun, and *'savasse'* or *'souasse'* swords, boxes, cutlery, jewellery, mounts and buttons.[46] The inventory of Van Hoorn lists under 'Jewellery and small items' Japanese and Tonkinese Sawasa as separate groups. The Japanese objects are fewer in number and more expensive. The inventory of Van Hoorn's father-in-law, the former Governor-General Willem van Outhoorn (1635-1720), also had Japanese and Tonkinese Sawasa as different wares, arranged under 'Silverwork'. It had both *a Japanese trouser-lace [ ] with souas mounting'* as well as *'a chints coat with tonkinese buttons'* and *'four tonkinese boxes with their lids'*[47]. On a portrait in the Rijksmuseum Amsterdam, Van Outhoorn wears a coat with buttons apparently similar to those in this catalogue (F.1.1 and 1.2).[48] Most other known inventories in eighteenth century Batavia we know, simply mention Sawasa without a provenance. Sawasa objects were commonly used and at the same time considered valuable. We find them in quantities under 'Gold pieces', 'Silver pieces' or 'Jewellery'. This implies that the objects at least contained gold or silver. In the VOC settlements in the seventeenth and eighteenth centuries, the value of artefacts was measured according to the presence of precious metals only. As exact prices are given for Sawasa wares, we assume that jewellers and VOC-assayers were somehow able to establish the silver and gold content. At least they were able to value the alloy. This confronts us with an interesting

the shogun, the head of the Japanese government, had a restrictive policy for weapons production and import. To evade regulations the Dutch possibly imported wooden models or drawings.[43] In Kaempfer's days this was also forbidden. It was illegal to sell or export: *'All kinds of swords, hangers and other weapons made in Japan, in imitation of those, brought by the Dutch'*[44]. Under these circumstances parts of weapons, such as sword hilts and scabbards, were possibly obtained by Westerners as objects of applied art. Despite all Japanese prohibitions to prevent such interaction, a taste developed in Japan for objects in European style, including weapons. As a result, *namban tsuba* (namban: southern barbarian, *tsuba*: sword-plate) were manufactured: traditional Japanese sword furniture in European fashion.[45]

Fig. 16. Painting of Willem van Outhoorn 1635-1720 (also spelled: Outshoorn/ Oudshoorn). Unknown Dutch artist, c. 1700. Rijksmuseum Amsterdam, Inv. No. SK-A-3769.

Fig. 15. Namban Tsuba. Japanese sword-guard made after European example, decorated with VOC-monograms. Rijksmuseum voor Volkenkunde Leiden, Inv. No. 3603-33.

problem. If we assume that Sawasa objects encountered so far, all look similar, e.g. entirely lacquered and gilded, how did jewellers in Batavia recognise the alloy? Normally they would assay the alloy from the bare metal using a touchstone or Lydian stone. However,

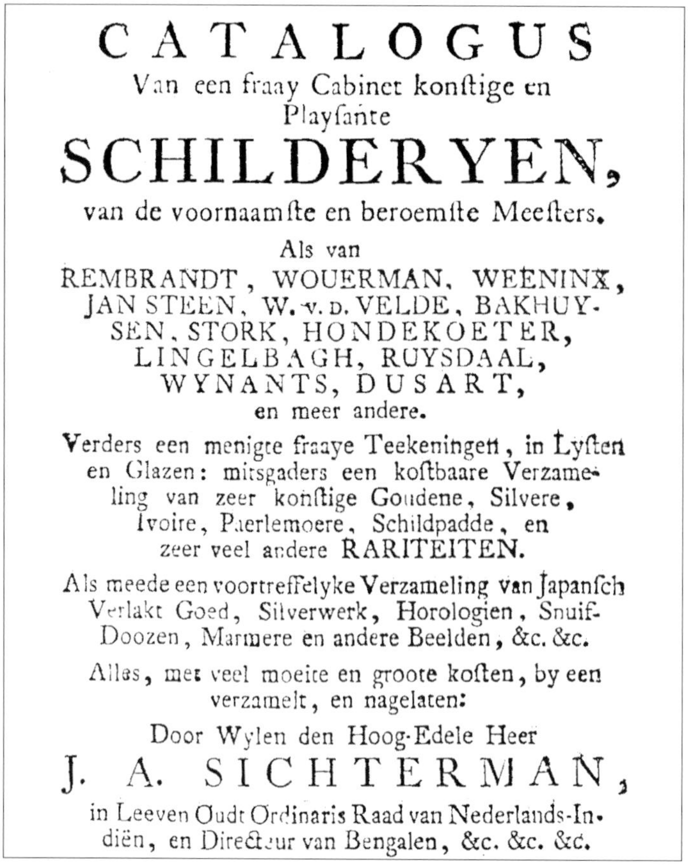

CATALOGUS
Van een fraay Cabinet konſtige en
Playſante
SCHILDERYEN,
van de voornaamſte en beroemſte Meeſters.
Als van
REMBRANDT, WOUERMAN, WEENINX,
JAN STEEN, W. v. D. VELDE, BAKHUY-
SEN, STORK, HONDEKOETER,
LINGELBAGH, RUYSDAAL,
WYNANTS, DUSART,
en meer andere.
Verders een menigte fraaye Teekeningen, in Lyſten
en Glazen: mitsgaders een koſtbaare Verzame-
ling van zeer konſtige Goudene, Silvere,
Ivoire, Paerlemoere, Schildpadde, en
zeer veel andere RARITEITEN.
Als meede een voortreffelyke Verzameling van Japanſch
Verlakt Goed, Silverwerk, Horologien, Snuif-
Doozen, Marmere en andere Beelden, &c. &c.
Alles, met veel moeite en groote koſten, by een
verzamelt, en nagelaten:
Door Wylen den Hoog-Edele Heer
J. A. SICHTERMAN,
in Leeven Oudt Ordinaris Raad van Nederlands-In-
diën, en Directeur van Bengalen, &c. &c. &c.

Fig. 17. *Auction catalogue of the collection of J.A. Sichterman, 1764. Rijksarchief Groningen, archive Sichterman, No. 605-A.*

most of the objects we have do not show any bare metal. A Batavia inventory of silversmith Hendrik Rennebaum in 1780 points in another direction. Among huge amounts of *'sawas'*, such as buttons, canes, hilts, buckles and all kinds of jewellery, there is a *'paper containing sawas filings'*. This indicates Rennebaum possessed the raw alloy himself in his workshop. The same list also mentions *'some sawas with a weight of 4 1/2 reals'* and *'an amount of sawas with a weight of 16 reals'* [49]. Moreover several Sawasa items are repaired or redone, others are fitted with mounts. This allows the conclusion that in late eighteenth century Batavia, Sawasa objects of all kinds were made or at least altered locally. Batavia had the facilities for local production, most artisans there were Asian. The city housed thousands of Chinese and a minority of Japanese ever since its founding.

Sawasa in Europe

From 1700, Sawasa wares were part of royal armouries and collections of curiosities in Europe, although the word Sawasa is never used. Most objects were introduced in Europe by means of the public and private trade system of the VOC.[50] We may assume other European trading companies, who had no access to Japan, such as the Swedish, French, Danish and English East-India Companies also imported Sawasa wares in Europe. For instance, the Chinese Pavilion of the Royal Palace at Drottningholm (Sweden), already had acquired some Sawasa wares in the eighteenth century.[51] In Holland Sawasa wares regularly appeared in collections usually described as 'Tonkinese chisel-work', 'Tonkinese chiselled work' or 'Cochin China work'. Unlike inventories made in Asia, where the wares were listed under 'Jewellery' or 'Goldworks'- Dutch inventories solely lists Sawasa wares under 'Curiosities'. The former VOC director of Bengal, Jan Albert Sichterman (1692- 1764) [52] owned a large collection of Japanese Sawasa. The auction catalogue of his estate listed under the heading 'Beautifully worked Japanese composition' twenty-nine Sawasa objects, among which coffee-, tea- and tobacco-utensils *'all of which excellently beautiful and artfully worked black with gold and with raised chiselled relief'* [53]. In most eighteenth century Dutch inventories and sales catalogues, Sawasa wares were described as 'Tonkinese'. Possibly, this word was used to suggest a general Asian provenance. Most descriptions show collectors had no precise idea of the nature of these objects. Already in 1704, a collection of the late Constant Sennepart included *'Tonkinese trouser buttons'* [54]. In 1710 a catalogue of curiosities formerly owned by Wouter Valckenier, a director of the Dutch East India Company, listed several Tonkinese tobacco boxes as well as *'a Tonkinese hanger, the scabbard with gold mounts'* and a *'powder horn with silver mounts and 2 Tonkinese knobs'* [55]. In the huge catalogue of curiosities belonging to Nicolaas Witsen (1641-1717), a famous collector as well as a burgomaster of Amsterdam, Sawasa wares were placed under 'Naturalia' in the subdivision of 'Rattan plants'. Among these, we find artefacts comparable to objects in this catalogue, such as: *'No. 1 A very large cane, covered with a polished ray skin; No. 2 A similar with a Tonkinese handle inlaid with gold, skillfully made; No. 3 A scabbard of a small-sword, [with] Tonkinese mounts and covered with polished ray skin [ ]'*[56]. Half a century later Roelof Blok (1712-1776), an employee of the VOC, left a collection of 'Gold and fancy goods'[57]. In the inventory a distinction was made between Japanese metalwork and Cochin Chinese tobacco boxes, probably both Sawasa wares: *'A copper tobacco box with gold inlays from Cochin China [ ] a set of black copper Japanese buttons [ ] an octagonal Cochin Chinese tobacco box with gold inlays [ ] a similar Japanese one; a black Japanese buckle with gold inlays and a set of shoe, trouser and necktie-buckles'*. At the end of the eighteenth century there was the inventory of Pieter Cornelis Hasselaar (1720-1797), a rich former employee of the Dutch East India Company, who lived most of his life in Asia. Here we find Sawasa wares mentioned under the category 'Silver-work, Tonkinese chiselled work, Chinese copper and other curiosities [ ]'. Again several artefacts resembled objects in this catalogue, such as a round tobacco jar: *'a fine and real Tonkinese chiselled round tobacco jar with a loose inside lid'* and spittoons: *'black chiselled spittoons*

with relief work'. It also has a censer with a *karashisi* on the lid: *'a very fine similar potpourri or incense vase, with a lion as a finial on the lid'.* Finally we find two oval tobacco boxes, one of which is decorated with silver relief work: *'similar oval pocket tobacco box, full with relief work; a ditto, ditto with silver work in relief '.*[58]

The status of Sawasa wares as very rare Asian curiosities in the late eighteenth and early nineteenth centuries is confirmed by a quite large group of Tonkinese wares in the famous Dutch Royal Cabinet of Curiosities. The objects came from the famous Royer collection, which formed the basis of this Cabinet in The Hague. Jean Theodore Royer (1737-1807) was a rich magistrate in Holland. He acquired his collection of Asian curiosities through his acquaintance with VOC-employees who worked or had connections in China and Japan.[59] A description of a table-watch in the Royer collection suggests a Japanese provenance of Tonkinese wares: *'A table watch, made in Japan (blue tongking, heavily gilded and with applied gold) giving Japanese and European hours, it strikes every hour. It is decorated on the indicator with an amethyst and contained in a*

rosewood box with glass on the front and back'[60]. According to the descriptions, the Sawasa wares are made of 'Tonkinese metal' or 'Tonkinese blue metal'. This clearly refers to either the surface coating or the patination. Here we transcribe some items from this group: *'A large urn [pijpkan], blue Tonkinese metal with loose foliage and leafs on the handle: neck and body and the compartments on the body are heavily gilded and inlaid with gold.*
Six similar cups and saucers as the afore-mentioned urn: the cups are gilded on the inside and the saucers worked with gold on the outside.
A cup and a saucer made of Tonkinese metal, fully gilded with flower work.
A pocket tobacco box, blue Tonkinese metal, on the outside with relief, showing sceneries, golden flowers, silver etc, the box is gilded inside.'[61]

Several of these descriptions literally fit objects in this catalogue, such as a the large urn, its cups and saucers and the tobacco box. Obviously black lacquered and gilt Sawasa wares are meant by these descriptions.

Tonkin and Canton

The Tonkin provenance is one of the big questions in this history. Rumphius already mentions Tonkinese Sawasa. We also have the Van Hoorn inventory where Tonkinese Sawasa is listed after Japanese Sawasa. The Tonkinese list is much larger than the Japanese but the artefacts are cheaper. This would imply that the alloy of the Sawasa wares from Tonkin was of lesser quality. In addition, we have the Roelof Blok inventory, mentioning Sawasa-like wares from Cochin China. The problem is that we have not found any sources that mention the production of Sawasa in the region of North Vietnam, then called Tonkin, nor in South Vietnam, then called Cochin China. Manufacture of Sawasa was certainly possible in Vietnam: for instance, in the international ports of

Fig. 18. *'The Studio of Tingqua, Canton'. From: Patrick Conner, 'The China Trade 1600 - 1860'. Brighton, 1986.*

Pho Hien and Faifo. Chinese junks and VOC-ships called regularly at Pho Hien, also called Pho Kagh, city of the strangers, along the Red River in the seventeenth and eighteenth centuries. The VOC had an establishment there in the years from 1637 to 1700.[62] Europeans and Chinese maintained a trade connection with Japan, exporting from Tonkin raw lacquer and copper and finished goods such as lacquerware and filigree. According to contemporary sources, Tonkinese lacquerware was of equal quality to that made in Canton and Japan.[63] The region had a long-term influence from both China and Japan. The country even harboured large colonies of Chinese and Japanese in places well-known for their artisan production.

The same assumption can be made about Canton. We have only circum-stantial evidence that Sawasa wares were ever made there. Canton was a well-known centre for the manufacture of any

Fig. 19a. Panorama of Canton, Chinese painting, mid-18th century. Rijksmuseum Amsterdam, Inv. No. NG-1052.

imaginable artefact. In the eighteenth century, the city, lying inland on the Pearl River, was one of the first industrial centres of Asia. It housed almost a million people and had many industries. On a large panorama of Canton one can see the industrial smog hanging over the city. Canton as a place of manufacture could explain a lot about our objects. Several of them show typical Chinese decoration. These objects, such as the tobacco boxes and the large urns, are very ingeniously constructed. Apart from Japan, one could expect this kind of technical craftsmanship in Canton. The city was noted for its high quality lacquer work and craftsmanship in all kinds of metals. Canton also was an important centre for the trade in metals from all over Asia. The Chinese and the Dutch exported alloys via Japan to Batavia, such as *tutenag* or *pak tong* (a silver coloured copper alloy)[64] and *tombac* or *tomback* (a copper and zinc alloy)[65]. Another important asset of Canton was that it could produce cheaply. It was not surprising that all trading nations called regularly at Canton. The European trading companies were allowed trading

posts by the Chinese on the island Jongsin-Seeluan in the river.[66]

Summary

The beginning of the production of Sawasa wares is clearly linked to the Dutch presence in Nagasaki. The Dutch demand, which started around 1690, seems to have been a matter of fashion with the wealthy European elite in Batavia. The relative scarcity of Sawasa objects and the restricted use of the word Sawasa, explains the fact that knowledge about Sawasa did not spread far outside Batavian circles. As far as Japanese manufacture is concerned, the initially limited supply of Sawasa wares may indicate a small production centre near Deshima. The typical style in which the objects were executed even points to manufacture in one or maybe a few workshops only. In the course of the eighteenth century, this style seems to have been copied by other artisans elsewhere. The provenance of Sawasa wares is not always clear. An explanation may lie within the Nagasaki trade, involving Chinese, Japanese and Dutch merchant interests. In this context, the

Chinese maritime trade network in Southeast Asia was probably the most important factor. It is almost certain that Japanese artisans made the weapons in our collection. Decoration and the techniques employed all fit the then existing Japanese skills and fashions. Other objects are possibly semi-finished products made in Canton or elsewhere in China or Indochina, brought to Japan by the Chinese junk trade. The Chinese sold many products in Japan because they could get a better price in Nagasaki. Subsequently, the wares could have been finished in Nagasaki or Kyoto[67], and exported again to Batavia and other ports. The Chinese trade also explains the spread of metalwork similar to Sawasa in Southeast Asia.[68]

The fact that Tonkin is persistently mentioned as a place of manufacture of Sawasa cannot be overlooked. It is possible that in some inventories the word Tonkinese is used for the whole of Asia. In other cases however an explicit difference is made between Japanese, Tonkinese or Cochin Chinese wares. At present we have no evidence which allows the positive identification of

Fig. 20. Chinese painted clay figure, presumably A.E. van Braam Houckgeest (1739-1801) who worked for the VOC in Canton in 1756-1773. Rijksmuseum Amsterdam, Inv. No. BK-1976-49.

Fig. 21. Fan with the inscription 'Sacred love' in the centre, made in Canton for an English or American customer. Ivory, cotton, glass, mother-of-pearl, 1780-90. Rijksmuseum Amsterdam, Inv. No. BK-NM-7007.

objects made in Indochina.

The end of the eighteenth century marks the quite sudden end of production of Sawasa wares in European fashion. The primary reason lies in the decline of the trade between Japan, China and Batavia as a result of the insolvency and subsequent collapse of the Dutch East India Company. The main buyers, the

Eurasian elite in Batavia, could not afford these luxury goods anymore. Trade in luxury goods would further be dictated by English economic interests and fashion based in India and Canton.

Cat.I.2.1 Black lacquered and gilt engraving, the engraved lines are made with hammer and chisel.

Cat. A.1.1 Detail of a cast hanger hilt showing gilt, patinated and lacquered surfaces.

Cat. B.17.1 Interior of a four-lobed tobacco box, showing gilding, chatter marks on the inside of the relief decoration and the soldered seam between the sides and the top of the box.

Cat. B.11.4 Black lacquered high relief decoration on the lid of an oval tobacco box, the relief is a chiseled appliqué.

Cat.C.3.3 Detail of a walking cane handle showing the gilding applied over the black lacquer.

Scientific analysis of metal alloys and surface layers of Sawasa objects

by the Netherlands Institute for Cultural Heritage Amsterdam

Peter Hallebeek

As a preliminary to an exhibition planned in the Rijksmuseum in Amsterdam the Netherlands Institute for Cultural Heritage in Amsterdam was asked to analyse a group of so called Sawasa artefacts. The Rijksmuseum had defined Sawasa wares on the basis of research in historical sources and some earlier analyses as objects of Asian export art, manufactured first in Japan and later in China and elsewhere in Asia. They were manufactured from copper alloys containing limited amounts of silver, gold and arsenic. These artefacts were decorated with ornaments in relief designs. The surfaces were partly covered with gold and other parts had a brown/black layer of lacquer. The shapes of the objects are often European or derived from European examples, while the decoration is from a wide range of Japanese, Chinese and European sources. The question was raised if the place of manufacture of Sawasa wares can be determined by establishing the nature and composition of the alloy and the surface layers. It was also hoped that a distinction could be made between objects made in the Japanese, Chinese and Tonkinese technological traditions, which were exported in the seventeenth and eighteenth centuries.

Therefore the following investigations were undertaken:

1. Microscopic investigation of the various surface layers.

2. Qualitative and quantitative determination of principal and minor constituents of the organic surface layers of a number of objects.

3. Qualitative and quantitative determination of the principal and minor constituents of the alloys and the inorganic surface layers. Composition of the various objects can be determined non-destructively.

4. Identification of inorganic components of surface layers and artificial patinas, remains of casting moulds and possible corrosion products.

Metals, surface layers and patina

The Japanese word *shakudô* (red copper) has been in use for a copper alloy containing between 1 and 5% gold. A comparable copper alloy is *shibuichi* which contains between 1 and 5% silver. In Japan a traditional method to colour surfaces of these metals has been in use called *irogane*. Artificial patina is produced by a chemical reaction with a hot aqueous solution of copper acetate, copper sulphate and alum. Each *irogane* produces a specific colour depending on the solution and the composition of the alloy. The word *shakudô* has a long history and dates back to the Nara period (710-784). All copper and copper alloys in the present context such as *tomback*, a copper-zinc alloy and the copper, silver, gold, arsenic alloys typical for Sawasa are, however, most often covered with surface layers of brown-black lacquer and gold.[1]

Lacquer

Exudates from various trees have been used in Asia since thousands of years for the production of lacquer. Lacquer is obtained from trees found in three Asian regions:

1. Japanese lacquer *urushi no-ki* from the *Rhus vernicifera*, the most important

component of the exudate is urushiol.

2. Chinese lacquer *tsi*, obtained from the *Rhus vernicifera* and also from *Rhus succedanea*.

3. Tonkinese lacquer *cay-son* tapped from *Rhus succedanea* which grows on the shores of the Red River.

4. Cambodian lacquer from the *Melanorrhoea laccifera*.

All types of lacquer are tapped from the bark of the lacquer tree. The exudate of the Japanese lacquer tree, *urushi*, is similar to latex and consists for 20-25% of water, 65-70% of urushiol, 10% glue-like substances, some of which contain nitrogenous substances, and less than 1% of the enzyme laccase. The water is allowed to evaporate. When the lacquer is to be used as a coating, usually a small amount of oil is added. Japanese lacquer is produced by stirring this fluid at a temperature of 30-45°C in contact with the air until the required viscosity is achieved. During this process water evaporates and components of the product start to polymerize. After application of the lacquer, polymerisation can be completed in two ways:

1. By drying the lacquer at room temperature in a moist environment which activates the laccase enzyme to produce a shiny film with a network structure, which is extremely durable.

2. By oxidation under the influence of ambient oxygen at room temperature; this process can be accelerated by heating the lacquer in an oven at a temperature between 110 and 180°C.[2]

Chemical and physical research on lacquerwork

If one wants to describe oriental lacquer within the context of known binding media it seems reasonable to look at the system as a water-oil emulsion (Gettens & Stout 1966). Drops of water containing polysaccharide and an enzyme are dispersed in an oily phase in which glycoproteins function as emulgators. According to recent literature no standard procedures are available for the analysis of *urushi*

lacquerwork, contrary to the situation for oils, resins, waxes, glues and proteins. In the research of *urushi* one has to take into account the high degree of polymerisation and cross-linking and the possible addition of inorganic fillers and pigments as well as organic substances such as drying oils or glues. Although research on fresh *urushi* lacquer and the mechanism of its reactions is relatively advanced and has yielded useful results, there is very little information on the effects of heating and ageing on the lacquer. If standard methods would allow separation of components, it should be possible to identify *urushi*. In practice however this is not possible because of the indissolubility of the *urushi* polymer system. The limited information obtained by analysis with infrared spectroscopy (FTIR) of an intact polymer system shows that this step cannot be completely ignored. This last method has not yet been tried in the ICN, pending the availability of reference materials (samples of various types of Chinese and Japanese lacquer, fresh and polymerised). Research with Fourier Transform Infrared Reflectography does give a readable spectrum, but comparison with available reference spectra from natural and artificial resins and lacquers has not provided any identification. The lack of reference spectrum data from Far Eastern resins remains a problem; in literature references are found concerning Japanese *urushi* lacquer on furniture, but the spectra of the lacquer on Sawasa objects show no resemblance to these data. This and other efforts towards identification of the lacquer show that the purpose of the analysis must not be the identification of all components present but rather the establishing of different patterns in different kinds of lacquer.

To break up the polymer network, drastic methods must be applied, such as controlled thermic decomposition (pyrolysis). One may hope that the network will always break at the same bonds and form the same fragmentation pattern. For a distinction to be possible, there must be

different patterns in different kinds of lacquer. The fragments then may be identified by mass spectrometry. Series of such tests have already been executed (Burmester 1983) and show great promise.[3]

Sawasa technology

Most Sawasa artefacts have been constructed from a relatively large number of separate parts. These parts were manufactured using many different techniques. Some solid and hollow parts of sword hilts, urns or lids and bottoms of tobacco boxes were cast, probably using lost wax techniques. In most cases, a large proportion of the relief decoration was sculpted in the wax model. After removal of the moulds the decorative surfaces were reworked with fine chisels and punches to sharpen the relief designs and get the minute granulated backgrounds, leaving characteristic chatter marks on the undecorated back sides. Other techniques were used to achieve minuscule punctures and dents prior to gilding and lacquering. In some cases ornaments were fitted with protruding elements which were soldered on, sometimes in *shakudô* metal or silver to further accentuate the high relief designs. Engraved decoration was made in both lacquered and gilt surfaces with a characteristic wedge-shaped line produced by hammer and chisel. Entire panels of relief decoration were fitted as appliqué.

Cat. B.10.2 Lid of an elongated octagonal tobacco box with appliqué of silver and shakudô.

The decoration and the frame surrounding it were chiselled from sheet metal and then soldered onto the surface.

The difference between entirely cast and appliqué ornament is often difficult to distinguish because the outlines in both cases have been crisply reworked with chisels. The same problem arises when comparing cast Sawasa with Sawasa manufactured in a repoussé technique. Many grips for sword hilts and cane handles, for example, have been cast hollow while frock buttons and side panels for tobacco boxes have been made in repoussé, achieving outwardly more or less the same result. In some cases, a central punchmark and circular grooves show that round objects have first been cast, then turned on a lathe. This is the case with small incense containers but also with the globular bodies of coffee urns. Not all vessels are made from cast parts. The ewers for wine, tea or hot water in this catalogue have been shaped from sheet metal soldered together with a single seam. Presumably their panels of relief decoration have been chiselled from the metal. The solder used for the seams and the appliqué work is always a hard copper-silver solder, nearly invisibly worked. Apart from soldered joints many other techniques have been employed to put Sawasa artefacts together, such as seams, rivets and sometimes split pins for the handles of ewers and urns. In most cases the lacquer layer, which seems black but has a brown hue, is applied over the bare metal in a very thin layer. The lacquered layer is worked to a matt gloss. It is quite remarkable that the lacquer surfaces of Sawasa wares show no signs of cracking or blistering. The adherence of the lacquer to the metal is impeccable except in a few more crudely manufactured objects where a thick layer of lacquer has been applied. The fire gilding of the relief decoration is quite thick. In the granulated backgrounds of the decoration the gilding has been left matt. The high relief decoration has polished gilt surfaces.

Conclusions

The analysis shows comparable data for the composition of most of the metal alloys and the various surface layers. The body metal contains copper as main component and gold, silver and arsenic as secundary components. The possibility that silver was used as an intermediate layer under the gilding was considered. This proved not to be the case. Analysis of the gilded surfaces of Sawasa wares shows traces of mercury, proving that a fire gilding process was used. The minute quantities of mercury remaining, show that the objects were heated for a prolonged period, thus allowing the mercury to evaporate. There is no indication for the presence of an artificial brown patina under the lacquer layer, such as is sometimes described in literature. The traces of iron and arsenic that were found can be explained by the presence of iron in the lacquer layer and not in the body metal; arsenic is a component of the body metal itself. The lacquer layers are brown, hard and quite thin. They do not contain gold, silver or bronze particles. In the lacquer an elevated percentage of iron is present, suggesting that the brown-black colour has been partly obtained by the addition of brown iron oxides to the lacquer. Identification of the lacquer is at present not possible because analysis according to the standard GC-MS procedures does not provide a characteristic pattern, which suggests that the lacquer has polymerised probably by heating to a high temperature. This method is described in literature. In one object (the tobacco jar Cat. B.20.1, Rijksmuseum Amsterdam, Inv. No. NG 1994-47 (CNO-132)) the remains of a hard substance consisting of 90% quartz and 10% silicate were found in cavities of the decoration, covered by the lacquer layer. Presumably, these materials are a remainder of the casting mould or they could have served to protect the lacquer during the gilding process.

Because all objects have fire gilded and lacquered parts, the question arises which treatment was applied first. Since the boiling point of mercury is 357°C, the proper temperature to evaporate mercury quickly from an amalgam lies around 400 °C. However, if enough time is available, evaporation of mercury can be achieved at a much lower temperature.

As far as the lacquer is concerned, the temperature can be raised between 110 and 180°C. It would seem logical to gild the objects first and then apply the lacquer. Microscopic inspection of the boundaries between the gilded and lacquered layers on the objects seems to prove that the lacquer was applied first. The technologies which were applied in the manufacture of Sawasa wares were available in Japan, China and Tonkin, and as such do not point to one or the other as country of origin.

(See Appendices 1 and 2)

Cat. B.20.4 *Inside of a comfit box showing gilding, soldered seams and concentric lathe marks.*

Cat. B.14.1 *Detail of the lid of an elongated oval tobacco box showing different decorative techniques such as circular punchmarks, dents of varying diameters, chiselling and surface treatment with black lacquer and fire gilding.*

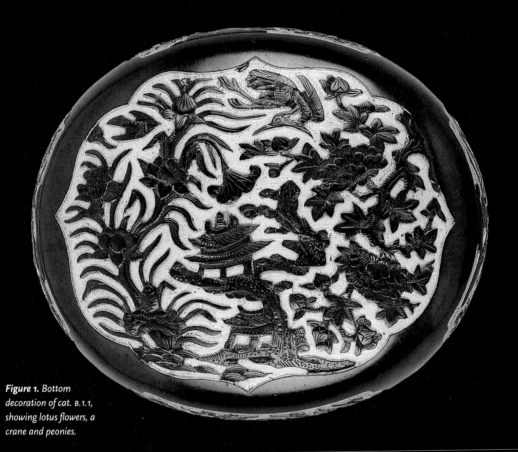

Figure 1. Bottom
decoration of cat. B.1.1,
showing lotus flowers, a
crane and peonies.

Decoration and symbolism
on Sawasa export art

Reni Krijgsman

A characteristic feature of the cultural interaction between Asia and Europe in the eighteenth century was the adaptation of European shapes and designs for Oriental wares. The time, energy and money involved in ordering these wares 'on command'[1], made them less attractive as articles of trade for the East India Companies. The Company merchants barely had time to check the overall quality of the cargoes and even less opportunity to give attention to the decoration of individual pieces. It is not surprising, therefore, that a large amount of export art shipped by the Companies, including wares with European shapes, was decorated in Chinese or Japanese style with flowers, birds, figures and landscapes. This conformed to the expectations of the public in the West, who still regarded Oriental art as something exotic.

Cantonese gold and silversmiths, a group highly responsive to foreign needs and influences, developed a distinctive style to decorate metal export wares such as Sawasa.[2] It was characterised by cast, applied or repoussé decoration against a matted background, the latter being a typical Chinese feature of ornamentation. The most common technique to give the surfaces between decorative elements such as pavilions, trees and figures a dull finish, was ring-matting. In this technique a punch was used to create small circles closely massed together, some so small as to be scarcely visible as distinct and separate. This matt-finishing technique went back to the

Tang period (618-907) and was one of the most positive indications of Chinese origin. Repoussé work, a technique which also had its roots in the Tang period, was created by punches and hammers used on the reverse side of the metal. After forming the main features of the design, it was often finished by chasing and engraving to sharpen the detail. The concept of engraving was introduced into Asia from the West. It soon found its way into the decoration of Sawasa.

Traditional Oriental motifs provided a rich source of material which was easily adapted for use in the export market. The majority of ornamental features used in the decoration of Sawasa originated in Chinese artistic tradition, which showed a distinct preference for depicting nature, and which was copied by the Japanese. In this chapter a general survey will be given of the most frequently occurring decorative elements found on Sawasa export art, and their hidden symbolic meanings.[3]

Trees, fruits and flowers

The majority of Sawasa objects were very similar in design using the Chinese concept of ornamental panels filled with naturalistic scenes. Animals, pagodas, boats and occasionally Asian or European figures were placed among flowering plants, such as peonies, plum and cherry blossoms.

The plum and peony belonged to the floral motifs, which symbolised the four seasons: the *peony* for Spring, the *lotus* for Summer, the *chrysanthemum* for

Autumn and the *plum* for Winter. Apart from the seasons, they signified several other things.

The *peony* (Fig. 1) was regarded as the 'Queen of Flowers' in China and symbolised love and affection, masculinity, female beauty, wealth, brightness and honour. It was an omen of good fortune and associated with the yang, or male, principle. It represented the third month in the Chinese calendar. The *lotus* (Fig. 1) symbolised purity, being so beautiful and stainless yet rising from mud. It was one of the 'Eight Buddhist Precious Things' and emblematic of fertility, steadfastness, perfection and prosperity. The fruit, flower and stalk of the lotus denoted the three states of existence, respectively the past, present and future. The lotus signified the seventh month in the Chinese calendar. The *chrysanthemum* formed the crest of the Japanese imperial family. It symbolised joviality, long life and duration. It indicated a life of ease and retirement from public office and was especially associated with the ninth month of the Chinese calendar. The *plum* (Fig. 3) was a symbol of longevity, beauty and purity and was indigenous to South China. It represented the first month in the Chinese calendar and was regarded the 'National Flower', because its five petals indicated the five clans which lived in China: the Chinese, the Manchus, the Mongolians, the Mohammedans and the Tibetans.

Together with the *bamboo* and *pine tree*, the *plum tree* formed the 'Three Friends in Winter'. This motif combined the symbolic significance of all its components, which were believed to remain constant and to blossom before spring arrived.

Bamboo (Fig. 2) was a symbol of longevity, owing to its evergreen foliage, and emblematic of virtue and fidelity. The *pine tree* (Fig. 3) symbolised longevity, endurance and strength,

because it was believed that its sap turned into amber after a thousand years. It was also emblematic of leadership because of its height. The *plum tree* (Fig. 3), another symbol of longevity, was added for beauty.

In the course of the sixteenth century, other trees and fruits were added to the decorative designs used in the decoration of export art such as Sawasa. For example, the *cherry tree*, the foreign *pomegranate*, the *peach* and the *willow*. The *cherry tree* (Fig. 3) stood for female beauty and was probably brought at an early date from western Asia. It was considered the 'King of flowers' in Japan, the equivalent of the peony in China. The *pomegranate* (for example Cat. B.2.2) was introduced in China in 126 BC and the Buddhist emblem of good luck. As it was full of seeds, it symbolised fertility.

The *peach* (Fig. 2) was a symbol of springtime, longevity and immortality. It was believed that the fruit of the tree only ripened every three thousand years and conferred immortality on those who ate

Figure 2. *Detail of cat.* B.5.1, *showing, from top to bottom, a willow, a pagoda, a peach tree, bamboo and Japanese figures.*

them. The peach was associated with the yin, or female, principle and had a sexual connotation.

The *willow* (Figs. 2 and 3) was also one of the symbols of Spring. As Spring was the season of erotic awakenings, the willow, too, had a sexual connotation. The majority of the floral motifs

Figure 3. *Bottom decoration of cat.* B.2.2, *showing a plum, a pine and a cherry tree, a willow and a pagoda on a branch.*

described in this paragraph appeared mainly in cast, applied or repoussé designs on Sawasa boxes, sword furniture and other goods. The trees, fruits and flowers raised from the ring-punched background were frequently surrounded by a number of borders, most of them being lotus or acanthus designs (for example Cat. B.17.1, 2, 3 and 4). The concept of placing the decoration within a border was typically Chinese rather than Japanese.

The floral motifs also appeared as engraved decorative scrolls on the rims or feet of cups and ewers, or between the ornamental panels filled with landscape designs (for example Cat. B.3.1 and 2). On Sawasa hilts and covers of censers, they sometimes appeared as continuous openwork scrolls. Occasionally, these motifs were used as naturalistic designs for spouts, handles, feet and finials of cups and ewers, such as the entwined blossoming branches, the bamboo spout and the lotus-leaf foot (Cat. D.1,2 and 3).

Figure 4. Detail of the bottom decoration of cat. B.1.4, showing a karashishi with gilt engraved details and butterflies.

Animals, birds and insects

One of the animal motifs that were used to decorate Sawasa objects was the *karashishi* (Fig. 4), or Chinese lion, which symbolised the power and wisdom of Buddha. In pairs of stone they originally served as temple guardians, being the Defenders of Law and Protectors of Sacred Buildings. The number of bumps on their head depended on the rank of the official whose building they were guarding. The *karashishi* resembled a Pekinese dog and was characterised by its fierce expression, large eyes and curly mane, its bushy tail and curly locks of hair on the legs. It usually had a cub under its right paw when it was a female, or an embroidered ball under its left paw in case of a male. According to one tradition, this was not really a ball but a huge pearl with which the *karashishi* was playing in order to calm its nerves. Lion-guardians of this kind were known from the third century onwards. On

Sawasa objects they prominently were featured as finials of incense burners, which were the only items that were not made after European models. Occasionally, they appeared on Sawasa boxes, either engraved or in repoussé designs.

As guardians of official buildings and temples, the *karashishi* rivalled the *dragon* in popularity. Combining all sorts of mythological and cosmological notions, the dragon was one of China's most complex symbols. Next to the *phoenix*, qilin or unicorn, and tortoise it was one of the four supernatural creatures. In sharp contrast to Western ideas on this subject, the Chinese dragon was a good-natured and benign creature: a symbol of Spring, natural male vigour, spiritual power and fertility as he brought rain, thunder and storm. From the second century BC onwards, the dragon was also the symbol of the Emperor, the Son of Heaven. As an emblem, the dragon

Figure 5. Decoration on the top cap of cat. F.3.3, showing a phoenix.

represented the continuous changes and variations of life, as symbolised by its unlimited powers to adapt to all surroundings. Cosmological speculation distinguished four kinds of dragons: first the heaven-dragons, symbolising the regenerative power of heaven; then the

Figure 6. *Detail of the bottom decoration of cat. B.3.2, showing two horses.*

spirit-dragons, which caused the rain to fall; thirdly, earth-dragons, which ruled over springs and water courses; and finally, the dragons which guarded treasure. In general, they were portrayed with a serpentine body plus feet and claws, as can be seen in the openwork design of the lid of a large Sawasa censer (Cat. E.2.1). dragon-heads appeared frequently in the decoration of Sawasa sword furniture.

The second of the four supernatural animals was the mythological *phoenix* (Fig. 5), usually represented as a bird with long tail feathers, part pheasant, part peacock. It was the emblem of the Empress and symbolised the sun, warmth, abundant harvest, fertility, good luck and longevity. The parts of its body symbolised the five human qualities: uprightness for its wings, humanity for its breast, virtue for its head, honesty for its stomach and sincerity for its back. The phoenix was believed to represent the male principle, but because of its name, feng-huang, which meant crested love pheasants, also of sexual union. It appeared mostly in repoussé or cast designs.

Although they belonged to the most commonly represented features of

Chinese and Japanese art[4], the above mentioned animals were not at all frequently found in the decoration of Sawasa. During the end of the sixteenth and the beginning of the seventeenth centuries, fabulous creatures such as the dragon and phoenix virtually disappeared as main themes in the decoration of export art, and were substituted by deer, birds and insects.

Apart from *deer*, also *hare, horses, monkeys* and *dogs* featured as decorative elements on Sawasa objects.
The *deer* (for example Cat. B.3.2) was one of the symbols of longevity and signified riches or prosperity. It was said to be the only animal able to find the lingzi, the holy fungus of immortality.
The *hare* was the fourth creature in the Chinese zodiac and symbolised longevity. It was connected with the moon, where it was believed to be preparing the elixir of immortality. According to Chinese legend, there were no male hare, and hare became pregnant by licking newly sprung plant shoots. The seventh creature in the Chinese zodiac was the *horse* (Fig. 6), which was emblematic of manhood. The *monkey* (Cat. B.11.1) was the ninth zodiacal character and symbolised the adulterer.

The eleventh animal in the Chinese zodiac was the *dog* (for example Cat. B.2.3), which, symbolically, was associated with the West.

Animals were often combined with floral motifs. A frequently occurring theme was the *squirrel with grapevines* (for example Cat. A.9.3). According to one writer[5], the vine was able to creep all over and cover everything, while the squirrel, in scampering about, did the same.[6] Other combinations were the *phoenix and peony*, symbolising the lover and the beloved, and the *pine and crane*, which symbolised the last years of a long life.
Besides being one of the many symbols of longevity, the *crane* (Fig. 1) was a symbol of wisdom. Other birds which featured in the decoration of Sawasa, were the *pheasant*, the *eagle* and the *cockerel*.
In China the *pheasant* was regarded as one of ill omen. If pheasants did not cry at the beginning of the twelfth month, a great flood was imminent. If they still not started crying by the middle of the same month, women became lascivious and seduced men.
The *cockerel* represented the yang, or male, principle and was supposed to have the power to change into human form and to inflict good or evil upon mankind. It was the tenth creature in the Chinese zodiac, and symbolised reliability, as it never failed to mark the passing hours.
The *eagle* (Fig. 7) figured as a symbol of strength.
Although most of the animals and birds were executed in repoussé or cast designs, on some of the Sawasa boxes they were engraved on the bottom or sides.

Among the insects which decorated Sawasa objects were especially *butterflies* and in one example also *bees*. A *butterfly* (Fig. 4), in Chinese called *die*, symbolised a man in his seventies, for no better reason than phonetic similarity to the Chinese word for seventy. Consequently, it was a symbol of longevity. It also signified a happy and unconcerned life and marital felicity. Represented together with plum-blossom, butterflies signified long life and immaculate beauty.

Bees were a sign of prosperity and stood for industriousness and thrift. On one of the Sawasa tobacco boxes (Cat. B.11.1), they were shown together with monkeys. As the word for bee, feng, was phonetically close to the word for preferment to a noble rank, this combination could be taken as meaning 'preferment to noble rank'.

Figures and settings

All the animal subjects and floral motifs described in this chapter conveyed the impression of a real landscape design with birds, pavilions, boats and occasionally Asian or European figures. The implied movement of the animals, birds and figures and the settings of the trees, pavilions and boats seem to have tempted the European beholders into believing they were allowed a quick glimpse at what life was like in the exotic East.

Among the figures that appeared as decorative motifs on Sawasa objects, certain types can be distinguished. First of all, there are Chinese or Japanese figures depicted in boats. In a few cases it is clear that these were fishermen for they were shown holding fishing rods in their hands (Fig. 8). In other examples they just seemed to be carrying goods or travelling from one place to another. Another recurring subject was that of Chinese or Japanese figures crossing a bridge, the figures always depicted walking behind each other (as in Fig. 2). The distinction between Asian and European figures was quite clearly shown. Europeans were depicted with trade goods, smoking pipes, wearing European hats, playing on musical instruments such as the trumpet, and

were occasionally accompanied by a dog which was associated with the West (for example Cat. B.4.2). On one of the Sawasa boxes, two figures, probably a Westerner and an Oriental person, were shown standing under a large pagoda (Fig. 9).

The pavilions and pagodas, which were part of the landscape settings, were sometimes placed on the branches of trees. This seems odd, but the theme reoccurred quite often (Fig. 3). The pagoda was a symbol of Buddhism, and, like the religion, introduced to Japan from China. Although temples were often represented in Japanese art, the depiction of a pagoda was rare. Even more unusual was the presence of a flag of Chinese type next to or on top of a building. Both motifs frequently appeared on Sawasa objects (for example Cat. B.12.2).

Apart from panels filled with naturalistic scenes, there were also scenes related to the 'pleasure quarters' displayed on some Sawasa boxes. These depicted Japanese figures, mostly courtesans with their lovers or apprentices, in interiors which were furnished with screens, cupboards, small tables and other household attributes (for example Cat. B.8.1 and 2). Occasionally, a Japanese tea ceremony was depicted. In some cases, the Japanese figures were applied in silver (Cat. B.15.1 and 2).

Because Europeans, for example Dutch merchants of the VOC, had contact with the women of the pleasure quarters in Nagasaki, these types of boxes would have made good mementos. However, it is unlikely that the traces of the ancient symbolism implied in the Oriental motifs were of major significance for the European

Figure 7. Engraved bottom decoration of cat. B.11.3, showing an eagle with spread wings.

Figure 8. Detail of the bottom decoration of cat. B.1.3, showing two Oriental figures in a boat.

buyers. Otherwise, these motifs would not have been used to decorate export wares such as Sawasa. The Chinese and Japanese craftsmen probably chose these designs because they were pleasing and deemed appropriate to the items on which they were used. The craftsmen neither turned to narrative painting nor to real life for their inspiration, but used existing ornamental tradition as their source. The introduction of Western figures and other elements in the Oriental designs only illustrated the craftsmen's wish to appeal to a foreign market.

Figure 9. *Detail of cat. B.1.3, showing a European and an Oriental figure under a large pagoda.*

The Catalogue

a

Hangers and Small-swords

Swords seem to have been among the earliest objects made for Europeans of Sawasa. Early visitors to Japan must have been impressed by the high quality of the metalwork, which was applied to the swords of the Japanese samurai. The servants of the Dutch East India Company who spent long periods in Japan, most of the time in confinement on the minute island of Dejima in the harbour of Nagasaki, had ample opportunity, certainly during their yearly trip to the Japanese court in Edo (now Tokyo), to become familiar with high quality metalwork such as the sword furniture the Japanese elite used to carry.

It is not surprising that, in the period of the first contact between Japanese and Dutchmen in the seventeenth century, both sides showed a particular interest in each other's weapons. The Japanese were mainly interested in European firearms, particularly artillery; the Europeans were evidently more interested in Japanese sword furniture, not so much in Japanese sword blades which, although of superior quality compared with

European blades, did not fit in the European tradition of swordmanship. The earliest examples of European swords prepared by Japanese sword furbishers seem to have been hangers.

European blades, that is, blades manufactured in Essen and Solingen for the Dutch market, were finished by Dutch sword makers with etched and engraved decorations and gilding. These finished blades were transported by the VOC to Batavia as trade goods. At first, these blades seem to have been mainly short and broad curved sabre blades of the type Dutch seventeenth century sailors preferred for their personal defence. Important officials of the VOC sent such blades to Japan to be fitted with elaborately decorated, yet stereotyped Sawasa hilts, probably by a few specialised workshops that worked from models sent from Batavia. They were probably allowed very little latitude in the shape of the weapon while being given a free hand in the decoration. These hangers were not only fitted with Sawasa hilts but also with Sawasa furniture decorated en suite with the hilts, mounted in ray skin or shark skin scabbards after the Japanese fashion of that moment. The utilitarian blades used on the hangers were gradually replaced by lighter, straighter and narrower blades more suited for hunting than for combat.

As a weapon for personal defence, the hanger was followed by the small-sword. By the middle of the eighteenth century, mostly small-sword blades were sent to Japan for furbishing with Sawasa furniture. It seems also that Sawasa sword furniture for small-swords was sent to Europe to be fitted to blades there. Just like in the earlier period, the Japanese made hilts of very few shapes but with a limitless variety of decorations. The Japanese sword furbishers and their clientele particularly favoured a type of boatshell hilt. Just as was the case with other Sawasa wares, the Japanese craftsmen seem to have continued using certain models of sword furniture over a long period. Thus, they must have looked quite archaic to people used to the latest European fashions. There are no examples of small-sword hilts dating from later than the last quarter of the eighteenth century. Therefore, it can be presumed that the market for such costly exotic objects had disappeared with the downfall of the Dutch East India Company and the consequent elimination of the mercantile Eurasian elites who used to patronise the Sawasa industry.

B.K.

Hanger,
Japan, last quarter 17th century

Private collection
Sawasa hilt, steel blade
Length hilt and blade: 67.3 cm.
Weight hilt and blade: 550 gr.

A Sawasa hilt consisting of three parts and a screw. The domed pommel is decorated with a panoply of armour and artillery. The background has been patinated to a brown colour. The grip has a trapezium form and decoration of spiralling floral scrolls separated by cordlike borders in gilt relief designs on a brown patinated background. The knuckle guard is decorated with two European soldiers in raised and gilt relief designs on a brown patinated background. The shell guard has a cavalry skirmish in a border of draperies and clouds on a black lacquered background. The inside of the shell guard has engraved and gilt floral scrollwork on a black lacquered background. The shell guard, knuckle guard and quillon are made as a single piece. The European blade is single-edged with two grooves and is engraved on both sides with scrollwork, birds, and human heads with the inscriptions, "Soli deo gloria, Amor vincit omnia".

Hanger and scabbard,
Japan, last quarter 17th century

Gruuthuse Museum Brugge, Belgium
Inv. No. 0.181.XXV
Sawasa hilt, locket and chape, steel blade
51.5 cm.
445 gr.

A Sawasa hilt with tortoise-shell grip. The two Sawasa parts and the screw of the hilt are similar to A.1.1. The domed pommel is decorated with a panoply of armour and cannon. The knuckle guard is decorated with two European soldiers in raised gilt relief designs on a brown patinated background. The shell guard has a cavalry skirmish in a border of draperies, leaves and clouds on a black lacquered background. The inside of the shell guard has engraved and gilt flowers within a gilt border on a black lacquered background. The grip is made from a solid piece of tortoise-shell fitted with a copper ferrule. The knuckle guard, shell guard and quillon are made as a single piece. The watered Indonesian blade carries the name of a Javanese nobleman with a gilt cartouche: "PANGERAN ADIPATI SETJADININGRAT" and can be dated back to the early 19th century. The leather scabbard has Sawasa mounts decorated with gilt scrollwork.

Hanger and scabbard,
Japan, last quarter 17th century

Legermuseum Delft, The Netherlands
Inv. No. 014612
Sawasa hilt, locket and chape (alloy in %: copper: 95.8,
tin: 1.6, zinc: 0.9, gold: 0.7, silver: 0.5, arsenic: 0.2,
nickel: 0.2, chromium: 0.1, lead: 0.03), steel blade
82.7 cm.
660 gr.

A Sawasa hilt consisting of six parts and a screw.
The domed pommel is decorated with black lacquered
flowering branches on a gilt fishroe background. The
grip has a tapering form and decoration of spiralling
panels with black lacquered borders depicting black
lacquered relief animals, birds and flowering branches
on a gilt fishroe background ending in a lotus border.
A ferrule between the grip and the shell guard has oval
cartouches with flowering branches. The knuckle guard,
shell guard and quillon are made in one piece and have
black lacquered relief decoration of branches and
landscape elements. The flat surfaces are decorated with
gilt engraved flowers and branches. The rim of the shell
guard is decorated with
snakes and lotus leaves.
The European curved
single-edged blade
with a single groove is
engraved with a sun, a
half moon and
astrological symbols.
The scabbard is made
of wood covered with
lacquered ray skin.
The chape and locket
are decorated with
black lacquered floral
and foliage scrolls on
a gilt fishroe
background.

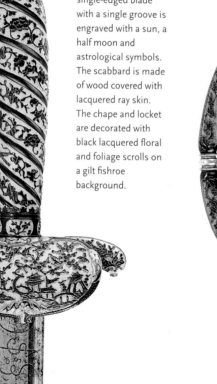

Hanger and scabbard,
Japan, last quarter 17th century

Rijksmuseum Amsterdam, The Netherlands
Inv. No. NG-1978-99
Sawasa hilt, locket and chape (alloy in %: copper: 88.3,
gold: 4.5, silver: 3.5, tin: 1.5, zinc: 0.9, arsenic: 0.4, nickel: 0.4,
chromium: 0.2), steel blade
75.3 cm.
775 gr.

A Sawasa hilt consisting of six parts and a screw. The domed
pommel and the grip are decorated with panels containing
black lacquered ornaments with plum tree branches, peonies,
chrysanthemums, pine trees, a pagoda, birds and butterflies on
a gilt granulated background ending in an elaborate lotus
border. The grip has a tapering form of hexagonal sections and
is fitted with a decorated ferrule and a knurled edged washer to
the shell guard. The shell guard is decorated with a central
cartouche surrounded by a rope-like border. On the upper and
lower edge is an elaborate monster-head. On the inside of the
shell guard are engraved and gilt branches and birds. The
shortened single-edged blade is engraved over one third of its
original length. The scabbard is made of wood covered with
lacquered shark skin. The chape
and locket are decorated with
floral and foliage scrolls on a
gilt fishroe background. The
hook is missing from the
locket. The sides are
engraved with gilt scrolls.
Many details of this hilt,
chape and locket are
similar to A.3.2

This sword was
presented by the VOC to
Johannes van Leenen
(1641-1721). Counsel
Extraordinary and
Ambassador to the
Persian Court at
Isphahan.

Hanger and scabbard,
Japan, last quarter 17th century

Private collection
Sawasa hilt, locket and chape, steel blade
70.6 cm.
472 gr.

A Sawasa hilt consisting of six parts and a screw.
The domed pommel and the grip are decorated
with elongated panels with black lacquered
branches on a gilt granulated background. The
knuckle guard and the shell guard are decorated
with similar panels. On top of the shell guard is a
monster-head and two paws. The inside of the
shell guard is decorated with various gilt
engraved flowers. The grip is fitted to the shell
guard with a ferrule and a knurled edged washer.
The blade is fitted in the hilt with a small gilt
rosette. The European, tapered and slightly
curved single-edged blade, is engraved at the
forte with animals of the chase, then hollow
ground with a sharp, wedge-shaped point. The
scabbard is made of wood covered
with lacquered ray skin. The
locket and chape are
decorated with peony
scrolls. The locket
has a flat frog
hook. Many
details of the
decoration
of this hilt,
chape and
locket are
similar to
A.3.1.

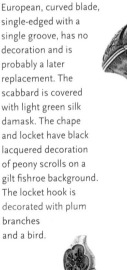

Hanger and scabbard,
Japan, last quarter 17th century

Private collection
Sawasa hilt, locket and chape, steel blade
76.1 cm.
585 gr.

A Sawasa hilt consisting of six parts. The domed pommel,
grip, ferrule and shell guard are decorated with black
lacquered relief designs on a gilt fishroe background. The
pommel and hilt have panels with pine trees, plum trees,
chrysanthemums, water plants, butterflies and pagodas in
profiled black borders. The lower end of the grip has a lotus
border. The grip is linked with the shell guard by means of a
black lacquered ferrule with lobed cartouches depicting floral
design and a knurled edged washer. The shell guard has a
heavy gilt border with grotesque faces and a large peony
flower in a circular rope-like frame. The back of the shell
guard has gilt engraved flowers and butterflies on a black
lacquered background. The quillons are vertically recurved
and end in gilt parrot-heads, which are decorated with black
lacquered relief branches. The
European, curved blade,
single-edged with a
single groove, has no
decoration and is
probably a later
replacement. The
scabbard is covered
with light green silk
damask. The chape
and locket have black
lacquered decoration
of peony scrolls on a
gilt fishroe background.
The locket hook is
decorated with plum
branches
and a bird.

A.5.1

Hanger,
Japan, last quarter 17th century

Private collection
Sawasa hilt, and steel blade
70.6 cm.
450 gr.

The hilt consists of four parts and a screw. The domed
pommel, knuckle guard, quillon and shell guard are
decorated with black lacquered relief designs on a gilt fishroe
background. The grip is spirally grooved and it shows scrolls
of plum tree branches, chrysanthemums, peonies, birds,
mythical monsters and a lotus border at either end. The grip
is fastened to the quillon block with a ferrule decorated with
four bracket-lobed cartouches depicting plum branches. The
knuckle guard is fastened to the pommel with a screw
through a gilt fish-shaped ornament. The shell guard is
decorated with a panel showing plum trees, peonies,
pagodas and a boat in a frame
of snakes. The black lacquered
high relief decoration seems
to be a separate appliqué.
The European blade is
slightly curved and single
edged with a single wide
groove. About one third
of the blade has elaborate
gilt engraving with the
inscription, "Amour fait
beaucoup mais Argent fait
tout" on one side and
"Les hommes font La
guerre. Et Dieu Donnent
La Victoire. Anno. 1687"
on the other.

A.6.1

Hanger and scabbard,
Japan, last quarter 17th century

Hanger and scabbard, Japan, last quarter 17th century
Staatliche Kunstsammlungen Dresden, Rüstkammer,
Germany
Inv. No. X 438
Sawasa hilt, locket and chape, steel blade
82.5 cm.
570 gr.

The hilt consists of four parts and a screw. The domed
pommel and the knuckle guard, which is made as one single
piece together with the shell guard and quillon, are
decorated in black lacquered relief designs on a gilt
granulated background. The grip has spiralling panels with
black lacquered scrolls of flowering branches. The ferrule
has a continuous relief frieze of black lacquered flowers. The
shell guard is covered on the outside with black lacquered
relief flowering branches and
birds in a foliage border.
The inside has a gilt
landscape on a black
lacquered back-
ground. The plain,
slightly curving blade
has one groove. The
ray skin scabbard is
fitted with Sawasa
chape and locket with
a frog hook, decorated
with flowery branches.

This hanger was
probably a gift from
Czar Peter the Great to
the Elector of Saxony
and has been kept in the
Royal Armoury in
Dresden since 1704.

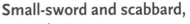

| A.7.1 | A.8.1 |

Hanger and scabbard,
Japan, 18th-19th century

Private collection
Black lacquered copper alloy with silver appliqués,
steel blade
Sawasa hilt, locket and chape, steel blade
61.6 cm.
410 gr.

The hilt consists of two parts. The grip and quillons are cast in open relief designs with silver appliqué work. The pommel is shaped as a grotesque head and on the sides are a male and a female figure and carnations in silver appliqué. The quillons end in silver claws. The shell guard that fits with a ring to the quillon block is decorated in open relief patterns, comprising of foliage scrolls interspersed with silver flowers in a basket. The Oriental blade is watered and straight, flat and single-edged. There is a silver gilt decoration on either side of the forte in the form of scrolls and Japanese characters. The scabbard is covered with leather, imitating ray skin. The chape and locket are decorated in open relief designs, comprising foliage scrolls and silver flowers.

Small-sword and scabbard,
Japan, c. 1700

Staatliche Kunstsammlungen Dresden,
Rüstkammer, Germany
Inv. No. VI-447
Sawasa hilt, locket and chape, steel blade
102 cm.
550 gr.

The hilt consists of five parts and a screw, and the pommel and guards are decorated with small panels with black lacquered floral scrollwork. Some details on the knuckle guard, quillon and the border of the shell guard are accentuated with bright gilded monster-heads. The shell guard is decorated with black lacquered and gilt open relief foliage and peony scrolls on both sides of shieldlike cartouches with black lacquered branches on a granulated gilt background. The grip has a spiral profile and is wound with gilt copperwire with Turk's head knots. The colichemarde blade is triangular in section and is decorated on the forte with scrolls of flowers and snakes. The wooden scabbard is covered with lacquered shark skin and is fitted with a Sawasa locket, decorated with black lacquered scrollwork on a gilt granulated ground with a locket hook decorated with a gilt mask. The chape has black lacquered decoration of floral scrolls and peonies.

A.9.1

Small-sword and scabbard,
Japan, mid-18th century

Private collection
Sawasa hilt and locket, steel blade
87.6 cm.
442 gr.

The hilt is decorated with black lacquered relief openwork with gilt animals such as hare, foxes, horses and dogs. The knuckle guard, which has a hare's head ornament in the middle, fits in a recess in the pommel. The grip has decorative openwork panels separated by spiralling gilt borders. The ferrules of the grip are decorated with fretwork. The lobed shell guard has a pronounced gilt frame on the inside as well as the outside. The blade is pierced at the forte and shows remains of blueing and a gilt inscription: "Spinola". The lacquered shark skin scabbard has a renewed chape and a locket decorated en suite with the hilt.

A.9.2

Small-sword,
Japan, mid-18th century

Private collection
Sawasa hilt, steel blade
93 cm.
446 gr.

The hilt consists of five parts and a screw. The pommel, knuckle guard, grip, quillon block and boat-shaped shell guard are decorated with black lacquered openwork with gilt ornaments showing flowering plum branches, peach branches and pine branches (the Three Friends), cranes, horses, monkeys and other animals such as an entwined dragon around the knuckle guard. The gilt ferrules are engraved with lotus borders. The double-edged blade is of flat oval section at the forte, changing to hexagonal and diamond at the point. The forte is gilt and etched with interlaced strapwork and an angel with a sword. The blade does not fit very well in the shell guard and is probably a later replacement.

A.9.3

Small-sword and scabbard,
Japan, mid-18th century

Rijksmuseum Amsterdam
Inv. No. NG-NM-TN-250
Sawasa hilt, locket and chape (alloy in %: copper: 95.8, silver:
1.3, gold: 1.0, zinc: 0.9, arsenic: 0.7, chromium: 0.1, nickel: 0.1,
lead: 0.03), steel blade
96.7 cm.
422 gr.

The hilt consists of ten parts. The pommel, grip, knuckle guard, quillon and quillon block, and the boat-shaped shell guard are decorated with black lacquered open relief patterns of continuous foliage scrolling, interspersed with branches, nuts and squirrels. The gilt ferrules are adorned with fretwork and profiled lotus borders. The grip has spiralling gilt grooves separating the foliate scrolls. The European blade is hexagonal in section. The forte has a gilt decoration of panoply scrolls and a laurelled human head on an iridescent blue background. In a cartouche is a spurious Latin inscription, "opiris victoria finis". The scabbard is made of wood covered with velum. The chape, locket and locket hook are decorated with gilt branches with nuts and squirrels on black lacquered open relief.

A.10.1

Small-sword,
Japan, mid-18th century

Private collection
Sawasa hilt, steel blade
99.2 cm.
575 gr.

The hilt consists of five parts and is decorated in European style. The pommel, grip, knuckle guard, quillons and shell guard are decorated in gilt and black lacquered relief designs on a black lacquered fishroe background. The lacquer appears to have been applied over the gilding, which seems to be quite unusual. The decoration consists of narrow foliage scrolls involving rosettes and fleurons. On either side of the grip is a stylised chrysanthemum. The shell guard is slightly dished and of rectangular shape with rounded ends and an inset cusped section on each side. The quillons are formed of foliage scrolls, running on one side into the knuckle guard that ends at the pommel in a sharply turned finial. The *colichemarde* blade is fastened to the hilt with a gilt threaded nut. The blade is double-edged and has a flattened hexagonal section at the forte changing to a diamond section at the point. The forte has etched trelliswork panels, scrolls and a Turkish soldier.

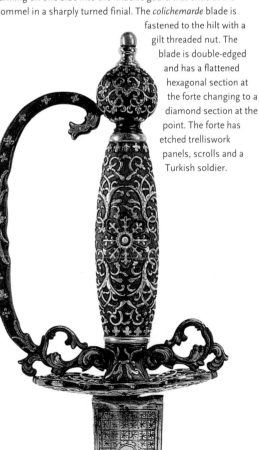

Small-sword,
Japan, c.1770

Private collection
Sawasa hilt, steel blade
87.6 cm.
344 gr.

The small hilt consists of four parts. The pommel, grip and guard are decorated with black lacquered openwork foliage scrolls interspersed with gilt animals and birds. On the guard is a central openwork panel with an ibex and a dog. The grip ends on both sides in gilt ferrules with lotus borders. The knuckle guard fits on one side in a recess in the pommel; on the other side, it has an additional loop guard fitted with a lobed openwork panel and a single quillon. The blade is hexagonal in section and waved, and has gilt engraved scrollwork over its entire length.

Small-sword,
Japan, c. 1770

Private collection
Sawasa hilt, steel blade
101 cm.
438 gr.

The heavy hilt consists of five parts. The pommel, grip, ferrules, knuckle guard, quillon block and shell guard are decorated with a continuous design of black lacquered relief foliage on a gilt granulated background. The grip has only floral and herbal designs. The pommel and guards show a combination of scrollwork with flowering branches with buildings and animals. The top and bottom of the grip are decorated with lotus borders. The blade is hollow triangular in section. The forte is blued and has gilt engraved decorations and inscriptions. In a cartouche is the motto: "Les Pucelles D'apresent sont à la mamelles". On one side of the forte is the inscription: "Abraham Du Cellieé Mr. Fourbisseur Francais dans la Calverstraat Amsterdam", and on the other: "Abraham Du Cellieé Mr Zwaardveeger in de Kalverstaat Amsterdam".

Small-sword,
Japan, second half 18th century

Private collection
Sawasa hilt, steel blade
96 cm.
396 gr

The hilt consists of six parts. The pommel, knuckle guard, quillon and quillon block are decorated with black lacquered relief designs of flowering branches on a gilt granulated ground. The shell guard is decorated with black and gilt openwork relief patterns of foliage scrolls and monster-heads, framing two small cartouches decorated with black lacquered relief designs of cherry branches and birds on a gilt granulated background. The grip is wound with twisted and plaited silver wire. The two-edged blade is hexagonal in section. It is decorated with engraved scrollwork and is inscribed on one side: "Ab. Du Cellieé mr fourbisseur dans le Kalverstraat a Amsterdam" and on the other "Abr Du Cellieé M Zwardveger in de Kalverstraat tot Amsterdam". This hilt is similar but not identical to A.13.2.

Small-sword,
Japan, second half 18th century

Private collection
Sawasa hilt, steel blade
83.6 cm.
358 gr.

The hilt consists of six parts. The pommel, knuckle guard, quillon and quillon block are decorated with black lacquered relief on a gilt granulated background. The decoration includes a lotus border around the top, and peonies, plum trees and birds around the bottom of the pommel. The shell guard is decorated with black lacquered and gilt open relief foliage scrolls and monster-heads, framing two small cartouches decorated with black lacquered relief cherry trees on a gilt fishroe background. The grip is wound with twisted and plaited silver wire and with Turk's head knots at either end. The blade is hexagonal in section. It is decorated with engraved scrollwork and depicts tulips, stars and a crown on one side and a ground paternoster decoration on the other. This hilt is similar but not identical to A.13.1.

Small-sword,

Japan, second half 18th century

Private collection
Sawasa hilt, steel blade
91 cm.
332 gr.

The hilt consists of eight parts and a screw. The pommel is decorated with very high relief gilt plum trees, pine trees, birds, insects and pagodas on a black lacquered granulated ground. The knuckle guard, quillon and quillon block are small and very slim, sparingly decorated with gilt ornaments. The silver wire wound grip is fitted with a black and gold knurled edged washer. The shell guard is decorated with black and gilt open relief work consisting of scrolls with snakes framing two cartouches with black lacquered flowering branches on a gilt granulated ground. The plain blade is oval in section at the forte becoming hexagonal and diamond towards the point.

Small-sword,

Japan, mid-18th century

Private collection
Sawasa hilt, steel blade
97 cm.
424 gr.

The hilt consists of six parts. The pommel, knuckle guard, grip, quillon, quillon block and boat-shaped shell guard are decorated with black lacquered relief openwork depicting continuous foliage scrolling, interspersed with various flowers. The gilt ferrules of the grip are adorned with fretwork and lotus borders. The two-edged blade has a flattened oval forte with etched and gilt decoration. On both sides of the forte is a ground paternoster decoration and an inscription in a cartouche: "Wm Hendr Roelvinck Mr Zwaardveger a Amsterdam".

Small-sword,

Japan, last quarter 18th century

Private collection
Sawasa hilt, steel blade
90 cm.
490 gr.

The hilt consists of five parts. The grip, ferrules, quillon block, quillon, knuckle guard and shell guard with black lacquered relief decoration on a gilt granulated ground in lobed cartouches of various shapes. The knuckle guard fits into a recess in the pommel. The decoration includes pine trees, weeping willows, plum trees, chrysanthemums, grapevines, bamboo, water plants, birds and a *karashishi* placed in the centre of the grip. The blade is hexagonal in section and blued at the forte, which is engraved and gilt with medallions and floral scrolls.

The Catalogue

b

Sawasa Containers for Tobacco and Other Stimulants

Tobacco came originally from the highlands of Central America. From there it spread to the northern and southern parts of the continent. It was first imported into Europe in the sixteenth century by Portugese merchants, who also introduced it into Southeast Asia. Initially, tobacco was valued for its medicinal qualities. In the seventeenth century, however, tobacco smoking and snuff-taking became increasingly fashionable, the latter even amongst women. Tobacco and snuffboxes were usually carried in a chatelaine or purse, for clothes with pockets were not in use until circa 1670. Large tobacco jars were used in the home.

The luxurious Sawasa tobacco- and snuffboxes, shaped according to European tastes, were commissioned by the Dutch East India Company. Receiving such assignments from foreign customers was no novelty for the Chinese and Japanese craftsmen, since they were already accustomed to catering for other Asian markets. However, although the boxes had European shapes, they were decorated in Oriental style. It is difficult to determine

whether a tobacco box was made by a Chinese or a Japanese craftsman, since the Japanese copied the Chinese.

The boxes are between 8 and 12 centimetres long. As analysis shows, they were manufactured from a precious copper alloy with gold, silver and arsenic. In general, they have a hinged lid, which must fit the rim of the box tightly so that the tobacco could not fall out or lose its aroma.
The hinge is attached to the lid and base by a hinge leaf. Often, one can tell by the hinge and the construction of the clasp from which period a box is dated. In the seventeenth and early eighteenth century the hinge leaf was more heavily constructed. The clasp was soldered to the inside of the lid. When the box closed, the clasp clicked into a slot

soldered to the inside of the base. During the course of the eighteenth century the hinge leaf became an integrated part of the lid. The hinge and clasp were usually replaced by profiled rims, which made opening the box much easier.

As comparatively few new ideas about the latest fashion in boxes reached the Asian craftsmen, various shapes of boxes were manufactured over a rather long period of time. Therefore, rather than categorizing the boxes chronologically, they are arranged in groups of similar shapes.
The first group consists of oval shaped boxes with curved convex sides. The lid is hinged and often has a heavy contoured hinge leaf. In general, the earlier examples from this group are smaller than the later ones. They are dated from c. 1660 onwards.
The second group consists of octagonal boxes with upright sides. Some have clipped corners. Most boxes have a hinge, either integrated or soldered on. The others have a detachable lid. The boxes in this group are dated from c. 1700 onwards.
The third group consists of elongated oval shaped boxes with upright sides. Approximately half of them have a hinged lid, soldered to the outside of the box. The remaining examples have a detachable lid. These boxes were manufactured from c. 1720 onwards.
The fourth group consists of four-lobed boxes, mostly with prominent profiled rims instead of hinges. A few examples from this group do have hinged lids, but these were added at a later date. The earlier examples are, in general, shallower than the later ones. They are dated from c. 1730 onwards.
There is one octagonal box with belly-shaped sides, dated c. 1750 or later.
The remaining objects in this category are harder to date, as are the purposes for which they were used. Apart from

tobacco or snuff, they could have contained stimulants such as pills and opium, or even matchsticks.

In general, all containers are decorated with ornamental panels on the lid, bottom and sides. These frames are variously shaped, differing from bracket-lobed to four-lobed and from octagonal to oval shaped. On most of the octagonal and four-lobed boxes they are arranged in groups consisting of a central panel surrounded by smaller, elongated frames. On the oval boxes there is generally one lobed or bracket-lobed frame on the lid and bottom, while the sides of these boxes are either decorated with several frames or a continuous frieze. The frames are filled with relief ornaments on a matt ground. On the lid this kind of ornamentation is sometimes applied in high relief, following the decoration on the bottom. Some boxes even have ornaments applied in silver.
Next to relief decoration there are also instances of engraved decorations, particularly around the sides of the octagonal boxes. There are a few examples where parts of the lid are engraved and in some cases there is engraved decoration on the bottom.

R. K.

B.1.1

Oval tobacco box

Private collection
Sawasa
Height 3.5 cm. x length 8.8 x width 7.3 cm.
Weight 115 gr.

An oval shaped tobacco box with a hinged
lid and curved convex sides. The lid,
bottom and sides depict traditional
Chinese landscape scenes with trees,
water plants, pavilions, birds and a figure
in a boat who is fishing with a cormorant
in black lacquered relief designs on a gilt
granulated background. The inside is
gilded.

B.1.2

Oval tobacco box

Private collection
Sawasa
3.4 x 9.5 x 8.1 cm.
194 gr.

An oval shaped tobacco box with a hinged lid and
curved convex sides. The lid and sides show
traditional Chinese landscape scenes with trees,
pavilions, figures, a goat and aWesterner smoking
a pipe, birds, deer and a squirrel in black
lacquered relief designs on a gilt granulated
background. The bottom shows an elaborate
crowned monogram after the European fashion,
surrounded by flowering branches and birds, done
in the same technique. The inside is gilded.

B.1.3

Oval tobacco box

Private collection
Sawasa (alloy in %: copper: 92.8, gold: 2.7,
silver: 2.3, arsenic: 1.0, zinc: 0.7, nickel: 0.2,
lead: 0.08, chromium: 0.04)
3.5 x 9.5 x 7.8 cm.
113 gr.

An oval shaped tobacco box with a hinged
lid and curved convex sides. The lid, bottom
and sides depict traditional Chinese
landscape scenes with trees, birds, two
figures under a large pagoda on the lid and
two figures in a boat on the bottom in black
lacquered relief designs on a gilt granulated
background. The inside is gilded.

B.1.4

Oval tobacco box

Private collection
Sawasa
3.7 x 9.3 x 7.6 cm.
140 gr.

An oval shaped tobacco box with
a hinged lid and curved convex
sides. The lid, bottom and sides
depict traditional Chinese
landscape scenes with trees,
pavilions and birds. On the lid are
two figures in a boat, one of
whom is a Westerner.
On the bottom is a black
lacquered *karashishi* with gilt
engraved details on a gilt
granulated background. The
cartouches on the lid and bottom
have an additional frame of black
lacquer. The inside is gilded.

B.2.1

Oval tobacco box with continuous decoration around the sides

Private collection
Sawasa
2.8 x 9.2 x 7.3 cm.
120gr.

An oval shaped tobacco box with
a hinged lid and curved convex
sides. The black lacquered relief
decoration on the lid and bottom
show traditional Chinese
landscape scenes with trees,
pavilions, birds, a horse and
figures on a gilt granulated
background. The sides depict
continuous peony scrolling,
done in the same technique. The
remaining surfaces on the lid
and bottom have gilt engraved
flowers and foliage scrolls. The
inside is gilded.

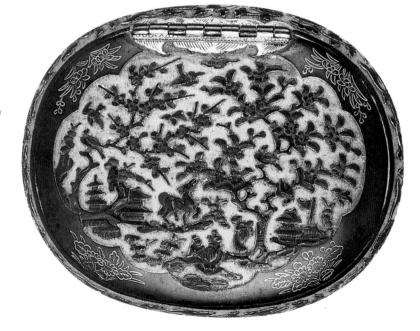

B.2.2

Oval tobacco box with continuous decoration around the sides

Private collection
Sawasa
3.8 x 9.7 x 7.6 cm.
173 gr.

An oval shaped tobacco box with a hinged lid
and curved convex sides. The black lacquered
relief decoration on the lid and bottom depicts
traditional Chinese landscape scenes with
trees, pavilions and birds on a gilt granulated
background. The cartouches on the lid and
bottom are oval shaped and have a thin rope-
like frame. The sides show continuous
decorations of birds, flowers and fruits, done in
the same technique. The inside is gilded.

B.2.3

Oval tobacco box with continuous decoration around the sides

Private collection
Sawasa
2.4 x 9.1 x 7.5 cm.
129 gr.

An oval shaped tobacco box with a hinged lid and
curved convex sides. The black lacquered relief
decoration on the lid and bottom depicts traditional
Chinese landscape scenes with trees, pavilions and
birds on a gilt granulated background. On the lid
two playing dogs are depicted. The sides show
continuous decorations of birds, flowers and
squirrels with nuts or grapes, done in the same
technique. The inside is gilded.

B.2.4

Oval tobacco box with continuous decoration around the sides

Private collection
Sawasa
2.9 x 8.9 x 7.4 cm.
129 gr.

An oval shaped tobacco box with a hinged lid and
curved convex sides. The lid and bottom both have a
cartouche within a cartouche depicting black lacquered
relief birds and fruits on the lid, squirrels and nuts or
grapes on the bottom and birds and trees in the inner
cartouches on a gilt granulated background. The sides
show continuous decoration of birds, flowers and
fruits, done in the same technique. The inside is gilded.

Oval tobacco box with continuous decoration around the sides

Groninger Museum, Groningen,
The Netherlands
Inv. No. 1997-0515
4.0 x 10.0 x 7.5 cm.
128 gr.

An oval shaped tobacco box with a
hinged lid and curved convex sides. The
lid shows a circular medaillion within a
cartouche and the inscription, 'Sibrant
Reyerz. Van der Burch' together with
his coat of arms. The remaining parts
are decorated with trees and birds. The
decoration is done in black lacquered
relief designs on a gilt granulated
background in the cartouche and on a
black lacquered background in the
medaillion. The sides show a
continuous decoration of birds, foliage
scrolls and flowers in the same
technique. The inside is gilded.

Oval tobacco box with an engraved scrollwork border

Private collection
Sawasa
2.8 x 9.8 x 8.0 cm.
267 gr.

An oval shaped tobacco box with a hinged lid
and curved convex sides. The lid and bottom
have a cartouche within a cartouche depicting
relief decoration of trees, pavilions, a
fisherman in a boat, horses, birds and a
butterfly. The inner cartouches show two
figures on the lid and a cockerel on the bottom
in black lacquered relief designs on a gilt
granulated background. The sides depict
traditional Chinese landscape scenes done in
the same technique. The remaining surfaces
are engraved and gilt with scrolling foliage and
birds. The inside is gilded.

Oval tobacco box with an engraved scrollwork border

Private collection
Sawasa
2.8 x 9.4 x 7.7 cm.
148 gr.

An oval shaped tobacco box with a
hinged lid and curved convex sides.
The lid, bottom and sides depict
traditional Chinese landscape scenes
with trees, pavilions, birds, deer,
horses and hare in black lacquered
relief designs on a gilt granulated
background. The remaining surfaces
are engraved and gilt with scrolling
foliage and birds. The inside is gilded.

Oval tobacco box with gilt decoration on a black lacquered background

Private collection
Sawasa (alloy in %: copper: 95.0, gold: 1.1,
tin: 1.1, zinc: 0.5, silver: 0.3, nickel: 0.2, lead:
0.1, chromium: 0.02, arsenic: 0.01)
3.6 x 11.8 x 9.2 cm.
144 gr.

A large oval shaped tobacco box with
curved convex sides and an integrated
hinged lid which closes with a decorated
clasp. There is black lacquered and gilt
relief decoration on the lid and sides. Some
of the parts in high relief have a patinated
blue-black surface, depicting fish, deer,
birds, insects, hare, a fisherman in a boat
and a phoenix on a black lacquered
granulated background. The bottom shows
one large phoenix, done in the same
technique. The relief decoration on this
particular box is embossed and chased
instead of cast. The inside has a corroded
black lacquered surface.

B.4.2

Oval tobacco box with gilt decoration on a black lacquered background

Private collection
Sawasa
2.6 x 8.7 x 7.4 cm.
121 gr.

An oval shaped tobacco box with a hinged lid and curved convex sides. The lid and bottom depict traditional Chinese landscape scenes with trees, pavilions, birds, Japanese figures, tradesmen and two Westerners with a dog, one playing the trumpet, the other smoking a pipe. The decoration is done in gilt relief designs on a black lacquered granulated background. The sides show a continuous decoration of birds, fruits and flowers, and are executed in the same technique. The inside is gilded.

B.5.1

Elongated octagonal tobacco box with a detachable lid

Private collection
Sawasa
3.8 x 12.9 x 5.8 cm.
178 gr.

An elongated octagonal tobacco box with clipped corners and a detachable lid. The lid, bottom and sides depict traditional Chinese landscape scenes with trees, pavilions, birds and figures in black lacquered relief designs on a gilt granulated background. The inside is gilded.

B.6.1

Elongated octagonal tobacco box with variously shaped cartouches

Private collection
Sawasa
3.7 x 12.2 x 6.2 cm.
253 gr.

An elongated octagonal tobacco box with a hinged lid. The lid has a central octagonal panel, surrounded by variously shaped cartouches. They are decorated in high black lacquered relief designs on a gilt granulated background depicting a traditional Chinese landscape setting with trees, pavilions, birds, flowers and a Westerner with a dog. The decoration on the lid is copied on the bottom in flat relief. The sides are engraved with a continuous band of foliage decoration. The inside is gilded.

B.5.2

Elongated octagonal tobacco box

Private collection
Sawasa
3.9 x 10.9 x 5.6 cm.
217 gr.

An elongated octagonal tobacco box with a hinged
lid. The lid, bottom and sides depict traditional
Chinese landscape scenes with trees, a figure in a
boat and a hare on the lid; and birds, squirrels and
nuts or grapes on the bottom in black lacquered
relief designs on a gilt granulated background. The
inside is gilded.

B.5.3

Elongated octagonal tobacco box

Private collection
Sawasa
3.6 x 12.9 x 5.6 cm.
224 gr.

An elongated octagonal tobacco box with an
integrated hinged lid. The lid and bottom depict
black lacquered relief decoration of deer and
figures in a landscape setting with trees, birds
and a pavilion, all on a gilt granulated background.
The sides are decorated with foliage scrolls, done
in the same technique. The inside is gilded.

B.7.1

Elongated octagonal tobacco box with flat bottom and curved lid

Private collection
Sawasa (alloy in %: copper: 95.6, silver: 2.6,
arsenic: 0.7, zinc: 0.5, gold: 0.2, nickel: 0.2,
lead: 0.09, chromium: 0.05)
2.4 x 11.3 x 5.6 cm.
147 gr.

An elongated octagonal tobacco box with an integrated
hinged lid. The lid has a central octagonal panel,
surrounded by smaller cartouches, decorated in black
lacquered relief designs on a gilt granulated background.
The decoration shows a traditional Chinese landscape
setting with trees, birds and a house. Three sides have gilt
engraved floral decorations. The bottom is not decorated.
The inside is gilded and shows chatter marks.

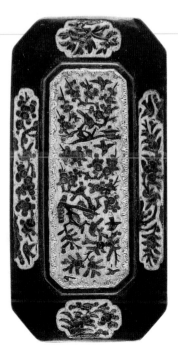

B.8.1

Flat octagonal tobacco box with clipped corners

Private collection
Sawasa
2.7 x 12.0 x 5.9 cm.
182 gr.

An elongated octagonal tobacco box with clipped corners and an integrated hinged lid, decorated in black lacquered relief designs on a gilt granulated background. The lid depicts an interior with a bonsai tree, a musical instrument and plates of delicacies. A Japanese couple is holding hands and a companion smokes a pipe on their left. The bottom and sides are decorated with traditional Chinese landscape scenes and foliage scrolls, with trees, birds, figures and boats. The inside is gilded.

B.8.2

Flat octagonal tobacco box with clipped corners

Private collection
Sawasa
3.0 x 12.3 x 5.9 cm.
239 gr.

An elongated octagonal tobacco box with clipped corners and a hinged lid. The lid consists of a top panel, decorated with a black lacquered and gilt lattice, within symmetrical scrolls and two mythological creatures, contained within a border of black lacquered and gilt foliage scrolls and flowers on a black lacquered granulated background. This top panel can be slid off, revealing an underlying high gilt relief decoration on a black lacquered background of two Japanese lovers and a maid in an interior with a screen and cupboard. The sides and bottom are not decorated and are covered with black lacquer. The inside is gilded.

Octagonal tobacco box with relief and engraved decoration on the lid

Private collection
Sawasa
2.4 x 9.7 x 7.8 cm.
227 gr.

An octagonal tobacco box with a
detachable lid. The lid is worked in black
lacquered relief designs on a gilt
granulated background, depicting trees,
pavilions and birds contained within a
black lacquered border with gilt engraved
foliage scrolls. The relief is a separate
appliqué soldered on to the granulated
background. The sides are also engraved
and gilt with foliage scrolls. The bottom
and the inside are gilded.

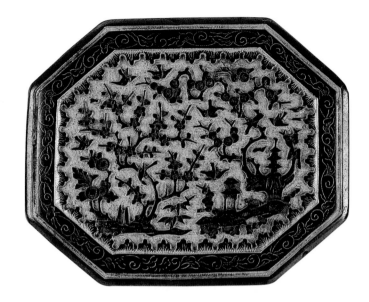

Elongated octagonal tobacco box with high and flat relief decoration with silver elements

Private collection
Sawasa
4.3 x 12.0 x 6.1 cm.
200 gr.

An elongated octagonal tobacco box with a
hinged lid. The lid is decorated in high black
lacquered relief designs on a gilt granulated
background heightened with silver and other
relief elements such as flowers, fruits and birds
in a traditional Chinese landscape setting with
trees, pavilions and a figure in a boat. The
decoration on the lid is copied on the bottom,
including the silver elements but in flat relief
designs. The sides are engraved and gilt with
foliage scrolls. The inside is gilded.

B.10.2

Elongated octagonal tobacco box with high and flat relief decoration with silver elements

Private collection
Sawasa
3.6 x 11.0 x 5.5 cm.
156 gr.

An elongated octagonal tobacco box with a hinged lid. The lid is decorated in high black lacquered relief designs on a gilt granulated background, with silver and gilt elements such as flowers, fruits and birds in a traditional Chinese landscape setting with trees and pavilions. The bottom and sides are decorated in the same way but in flat relief designs. The silver hinge is gilded and attached over the decoration by six rivets. The inside is gilded.

B.10.3

Elongated octagonal tobacco box with high and flat relief decoration with silver elements

Private collection
Sawasa
3.9 x 10.4 x 5.3 cm.
140 gr.

An elongated octagonal tobacco box with a detachable lid. The lid is decorated in high black lacquered relief designs on a gilt granulated background, with silver elements such as flowers, fruits and birds in a traditional Chinese landscape setting with trees and pavilions. The bottom and sides are decorated in the same way but in flat relief designs. The inside is gilded.

B.10.4

Elongated four-lobed tobacco box with high and flat relief decoration with silver elements

Private collection
Sawasa
2.8 x 12.5 x 6.7 cm.
171 gr.

An elongated four-lobed tobacco box with a detachable lid. The lid is decorated in high black lacquered relief designs on a gilt granulated background, with silver and gilt elements such as flowers, fruits and birds in a landscape setting with trees and pavilions. The decoration on the lid is copied on the bottom, including the silver and gilt elements, in flat relief designs. The sides are decorated with black lacquered foliage patterns on a gilt granulated background, with gilt elements. The inside is gilded.

B.11.1

Elongated oval tobacco box with engraved decoration on the bottom

Private collection
Sawasa
2.6 x 11.8 x 5.6 cm.
154 gr.

A flat, elongated oval shaped tobacco box with a detachable lid. The lid depicts traditional Chinese landscape scenes with trees, birds, deer and monkeys, one of which is disturbing a bees' nest with a stick in black lacquered relief designs on a gilt granulated background. The bottom of the box has gilt engraved decoration on a black lacquered background, showing a seascape with trees, birds, fish, figures with a fishing rod and a line, and a figure with a net in a boat with birds flying over it. The sides are not decorated but have gilt profiled rims. The inside is gilded.

B.11.2

Elongated oval tobacco box with engraved decoration on the bottom

Private collection
Sawasa
2.7 x 12.3 x 5.2 cm.
227 gr.

A flat, elongated oval shaped tobacco box with a hinged lid. The lid depicts traditional Chinese landscape scenes with trees, pavilions, birds, a boat and two figures in black lacquered appliqués on a gilt granulated background. The bottom of the box has gilt engraved decoration on a black lacquered background, showing an eagle with spread wings. The sides, which have silver profiled rims and a silver hinge, depict decoration of birds, done in the same technique. The inside is gilded. The decoration and technique of this box is very simular to A.11.3 and A.11.4. This suggests that these boxes were made in the same workshop.

B.11.3

Elongated oval tobacco box with engraved decoration on the bottom

Private collection
Sawasa
2.8 x 12.3 x 5.1 cm.
190 gr.

A flat, elongated oval shaped tobacco box with a hinged lid. The lid depicts traditional Chinese landscape scenes with trees, pavilions, birds, deer and a boat in black lacquered and gilt appliqués on a gilt granulated background. The bottom of the box has gilt engraved decoration on a black lacquered background, depicting an eagle with spread wings. The sides have gilt profiled rims and a hinge that is attached to the inside by six rivets. They are decorated with birds, including a hen and a cockerel, done in the same technique. The inside is gilded.

B.11.4

Elongated oval tobacco box with engraved decoration on the bottom

Private collection
Sawasa
2.7 x 11.7 x 6.2 cm.
182 gr.

A flat, elongated oval shaped tobacco box with a hinged lid. The lid depicts traditional Chinese landscape scenes with trees, pavilions, birds, deer and a boat in black lacquered appliqués on a gilt granulated background. The bottom of the box has gilt engraved decoration on a black lacquered background, depicting an eagle with spread wings. The sides, which have gilt profiled rims and a hinge that has been soldered on in a later period, are decorated with birds, done in the same technique. The inside is gilded.

Elongated oval tobacco box with a detachable lid

Private collection
Sawasa
3.0 x 12.0 x 7.8 cm.
269 gr.

An elongated oval shaped tobacco box with a detachable lid. The lid is worked in gilt relief designs on a gilt granulated background, depicting a fortified palace and a figure in a boat in a landscape setting with birds and trees, presented within three black lacquered oval frames. The bottom and sides are not decorated. The inside is gilded. The gilding on the bottom and sides is worn.

Elongated oval tobacco box with a detachable lid

Private collection
Sawasa
3.3 x 11.5 x 8.3 cm.
288 gr.

An elongated oval shaped tobacco box with a detachable lid. The lid is worked in gilt relief designs on a gilt granulated background, depicting birds and trees in a landscape setting with pavilions. The decoration is contained within a black lacquered oval border with variously shaped cartouches, some of them engraved and gilt, some of them decorated with gilt relief designs on a gilt granulated background. The rim around the lid is engraved with fretwork; the sides with continuous peony scrollwork. The bottom is not decorated. The inside is gilded. The gilding on the outside is worn.

B.12.3

Elongated oval tobacco box with a detachable lid

Private collection
Sawasa
2.8 x 10.7 x 5.3 cm.
165 gr.

An elongated oval shaped tobacco box with a detachable lid. The lid is worked in high gilt relief designs on a gilt granulated background, depicting flowers, trees, birds and a pavilion in a landscape setting, contained within a black lacquered oval border. The bottom and sides are not decorated. The inside is gilded. The gilding is worn.

B.13.1

Elongated oval tobacco box with a figurative design

Private collection
Sawasa
3.4 x 11.6 x 6.6 cm.
194 gr.

An elongated oval shaped tobacco box with a detachable lid. The lid and bottom are decorated with continuous black lacquered scrolling foliage, with five silver inlaid flowers on a gilt granulated background. The sides are decorated with running flowers and foliage done in the same technique. The inside is gilded.

B.13.2

Elongated oval tobacco box with a figurative design

Private collection
Sawasa
3.0 x 11.8 x 7.5 cm.
177 gr.

An elongated oval shaped tobacco box with a detachable lid. The lid has a circular cartouche with a black lacquered and gilt rose decoration in the centre. From there twelve elongated panels radiate, with black lacquered relief decoration of trees, fruits, flowers and birds on a gilt granulated background. The sides show four cartouches, decorated with black lacquered foliage scrolls on a gilt granulated background. The black lacquered bottom has no decoration. The inside is gilded and punched with chatter marks.

Elongated oval tobacco box with non-traditional landscape scenes

Private collection
Sawasa
2.9 x 13.0 x 5.4 cm.
192 gr.

An elongated oval shaped tobacco box with a hinged lid. The lid has gilt decoration of shipping in a black lacquered estuary and landscape scenes with buffaloes, rocks, trees, bridges and a pavilion, done in gold and black lacquer on a gilt granulated background. The rocks in the landscape have very finely gilded indentations. The bottom has gilt engraved decoration of two tigers. The sides, which have gilt profiled rims and an exquisitely formed and decorated hinge, show gilt engraved decoration of flowers and foliage scrolls. The inside is gilded and punched with chatter marks.

Elongated oval tobacco box with non-traditional landscape scenes

Private collection
Sawasa
3.2 x 12.6 x 5.5 cm.
176 gr.

An elongated oval shaped tobacco box with a hinged lid. The lid is decorated with a mountain landscape with trees, plants, deer, a lamb and several shacks, in gilt relief designs. The bottom is gilt engraved with flowers, rocks and butterflies on a gilt background. The sides, constructed from layers of sheet metal soldered together, have a very finely granulated background for separately applied ornaments in cartouches with gilt borders. A gilt hinge is attached to the inside with six rivets. The inside is gilded.

B.14.3

Elongated octagonal tobacco box with non-traditional landscape scenes

Private collection
Sawasa (alloy in %:
copper: 96.9, silver: 1.5,
zinc: 0.5, arsenic: 0.4,
gold: 0.3, lead: 0.1, tin:
0.1, nickel: 0.1,
chromium: 0.08)
3.1 x 11.1 x 5.4 cm.
124 gr.

An elongated octagonal tobacco box with belly-shaped sides and a hinged lid. The lid closes with a movable clasp and depicts a harbour scene, done in gilt relief designs on a black lacquered background with ships, a tree, a lantern and a row of houses in the background. The bottom shows a gilt engraved decoration of a phoenix or pheasant perched on a tree on a black lacquered background. The sides are decorated with a continuous gilt engraved vine scroll. One side has a small gilt push button to open the box. The inside is gilded. The decoration may be emblematical of commerce.

B.15.1

Four-lobed tobacco box with silver applied figures on the lid

Private collection
Sawasa
3.6 x 11.3 x 6.3 cm.
193 gr.

A four-lobed box with a detachable lid. The lid is decorated in black lacquered relief designs on a gilt granulated background with two appliqué silver Japanese figures in an interior with a screen, a dumb waiter and a cat. The cartouches on the sides are decorated in a more traditional way with foliage scrolls. The bottom is decorated in the same way as the lid, except for the silver appliqué figures and shows an interior with a Japanese courtesan with her maid combing her hair in front of a mirror. The inside is gilded.

Elongated octagonal tobacco box with silver applied figures on the lid

Private collection
Sawasa
3.8 x 10.7 x 5.2 cm.
188 gr.

An elongated octagonal tobacco box with an integrated hinged lid. The lid is decorated with an interior scene depicting a screen, drinking utensils and a plant in black lacquered relief designs on a gilt background with three appliqué silver figures in a tea ceremony: a Japanese man and woman playing on musical instruments and a maid on their right. The cartouches on the sides, as well as the decoration on the bottom, show traditional Chinese landscape scenes with trees, a pavilion, birds and a figure in a boat in black lacquered relief designs on a gilt granulated background. The inside is gilded.

Four-lobed tobacco box

Private collection
Sawasa
4.4 x 12.1 x 6.1 cm.
190 gr.

An elongated four-lobed tobacco box with a detachable lid. The lid is worked in gilt relief designs on a gilt granulated background, depicting trees, a pavilion, birds and a figure in a boat in a landscape setting, contained within a black lacquered border with cartouches. The decoration on the lid is copied on the bottom. The sides are composed of two layers of metal, the outer layer carrying the decoration of gilt engraved foliage scolls on a black lacquered background with gilt profiled rims. The inside is gilded.

Elongated four-lobed tobacco box with high and flat relief decoration

Private collection
Sawasa
4.2 x 11.9 x 6.0 cm.
196 gr.

An elongated four-lobed tobacco box with a detachable lid. The lid has a large panel and four cartouches, decorated respectively in high and flat black lacquered relief designs on a gilt granulated background, depicting traditional Chinese landscape scenes with trees, pavilions and birds. The bottom is decorated in the same way, except it is done in flat relief designs. The remaining surfaces on the lid, bottom and sides have gilt engraved foliage scrolls on a black lacquered background. The lid and bottom have gilt profiled rims. The inside is gilded.

Elongated four-lobed tobacco box with high and flat relief decoration

Private collection
Sawasa
4.1 x 11.9 x 6.2 cm.
213 gr.

An elongated four-lobed tobacco box with a hinged lid. The hinge is attached to the box over the decoration with six rivets. The lid has a large panel and four cartouches decorated respectively in high and flat black lacquered relief designs on a gilt granulated background, depicting traditional Chinese landscape scenes with trees, pavilions, birds and a figure in a boat. The bottom is decorated in the same way, except it is done in flat relief designs. The sides are decorated with gilt engraved foliage scrolls on a black lacquered background. The inside is gilded.

Elongated four-lobed tobacco box with high and flat relief decoration

Private collection
Sawasa (alloy in %: copper: 94.0, gold: 1.9, silver: 1.4, zinc: 0.7,
arsenic: 0.4, nickel: 0.2, chromium: 0.08, lead: 0.02)
4.0 x 12.0 x 6.2 cm.
239 gr.

An elongated four-lobed tobacco box with a detachable lid. The lid has a large panel and four cartouches decorated respectively in high and flat black lacquered relief designs on a gilt granulated background, depicting traditional Chinese landscape scenes with trees, pavilions, birds and a figure in a boat. The bottom is decorated in the same way, except it is done in flat relief designs. The sides are decorated with gilt engraved foliage scrolls on a black lacquered background. The inside is gilded.

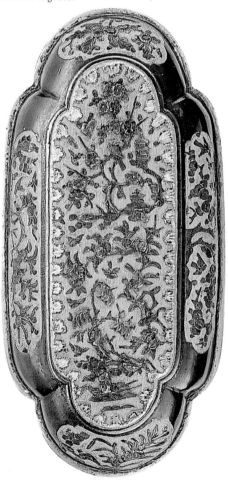

B.17.4

Elongated four-lobed tobacco box with high and flat relief decoration

Private collection
Sawasa
3.8 x 12.1 x 6.1 cm.
230 gr.

An elongated four-lobed tobacco box with a hinged lid. The hinge is attached to the box over the decoration with nine rivets and is evidently a later addition. The lid has a large panel and four cartouches decorated respectively in high and flat black lacquered relief designs on a gilt granulated background, depicting traditional Chinese landscape scenes with trees, pavilions, birds and a figure in a boat. Some parts of the high relief decoration show a shiny blue-black patina where the lacquer is worn down, proving that this metal is at least a copper-gold alloy. The bottom is decorated in the same way, except it is done in flat relief designs. The sides are engraved and gilt with foliage scrolls on a black lacquered background. The inside is gilded and shows indentations.

B.18.1

Small oval tobacco box

Private collection
Sawasa
1.5 x 4.7 x 3.6 cm.
26 gr.

A small oval shaped tobacco box with a hinged lid and curved convex sides. The lid depicts traditional Chinese landscape scenes with trees, pavilions and dogs; two figures surrounded by peonies on the bottom; and squirrels, nuts or grapes and water plants around the sides. The decoration is done in black lacquered relief designs on a gilt granulated background. The remaining surfaces are engraved and gilt with decorative scrolls on a black lacquered background. The inside is gilded.

B.18.2

Small oval tobacco box

Private collection
Sawasa
2.3 x 6.1 x 4.9 cm.
41 gr.

A small oval shaped tobacco box with a hinged lid and curved convex sides. The lid and bottom are worked in gilt relief designs on a gilt granulated background, depicting birds, peonies, a tree, a pavilion and a butterfly, contained within a black lacquered border. The sides are engraved and gilt with cartouches depicting birds, fruit trees and flowers. Under the hinge are two holes, reinforced with silver rings and rosettes to adapt the box for use as a *tabako-ire*. The inside is gilded.

B.18.3

Small oval tobacco box with high relief decoration

Private collection
Sawasa
1.9 x 5.1 x 4.1 cm.
35 gr.

A small oval shaped tobacco box with a hinged lid and
curved convex sides. There is high black lacquered
relief decoration on the sides, lid and bottom depicting
traditional Chinese landscape scenes with trees,
pavilions, birds, a deer and two figures on a bridge on
a gilt granulated background. The sides have
continuous decoration of flowers and birds, done in
the same technique. Some of the highest relief
elements have been soldered on. The inside is gilded.

B.18.4

Small oval tobacco box

Private collection
Sawasa
3.2 x 5.1 x 4.1 cm.
33 gr.

A small oval shaped tobacco box with a hinged lid and
curved convex sides. The lid, bottom and sides depict
traditional Chinese landscape scenes in bracket-lobed
cartouches, with trees, pavilions and birds in black
lacquered relief designs on a gilt granulated background.
A ring attached to a black lacquered rosette has been
fitted onto the bottom in a later period, apparently to use
the box as a *tabako-ire*. The inside is gilded.

B.18.5

Miniature oval box

Private collection
Sawasa
1.1 x 2.5 x 2.2 cm.
8.5 gr.

A miniature oval shaped box with a hinged
lid and curved convex sides. There are
bracket-lobed cartouches on both the lid
and bottom, depicting black lacquered relief
birds and trees on a gilt granulated
background. The sides are engraved and
gilt with foliage scrolls. The inside is gilded.

Small four-lobed tobacco box

Private collection
Sawasa
2.1 x 6.6 x 4.4 cm.
63 gr

A small four-lobed tobacco box with a flat bottom and a detachable lid. Four holes in the sides of the bottom and lid suggest a missing hinge. The lid and bottom both have a central four-lobed panel surrounded by smaller cartouches decorated in black lacquered relief designs on a gilt granulated background. The decoration depicts a traditional Chinese landscape setting with trees, pavilions, birds and a figure in a boat. The sides are engraved and gilt with foliage scrolls and flowers. The inside is gilded.

Book-shaped box

Private collection
Sawasa
1.5 x 7.5 x 4.7 cm.
82 gr.

A book-shaped box with an integrated hinged lid with a wide inner rim. The front and back are decorated with trees, pavilions and birds in high black lacquered relief designs on a gilt granulated background, contained within a double frame. The spine of the book shows gilt ribs and gilt engraved flax motifs. The inside is gilded. The box seemingly opens on the wrong side, probably because the Asian craftsman was unfamiliar with books of this type.

B.19.2

Book-shaped box

Private collection
Sawasa (alloy in %: copper: 94.4, silver: 2.6,
gold: 1.1, zinc: 0.9, arsenic: 0.4, nickel: 0.3,
chromium: 0.08)
1.7 x 7.4 x 4.8 cm.
118 gr.

A book-shaped box with an integrated
hinged lid. The front and back are
decorated with trees, pavilions and birds in
high black lacquered relief designs on a gilt
granulated background. Some of the high
relief flowers have been soldered on. The
spine of the book shows gilt ribs and gilt
engraved flax motifs.The inside is gilded on
the lid and painted black on the bottom.
The box opens on the wrong side like B.19.1

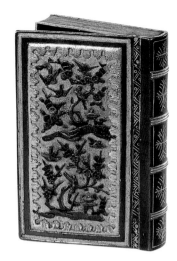

B.20.1

Large circular tobacco jar

Rijksmuseum Amsterdam, The Netherlands
Inv. No. NG-1994-47 (CNO-132)
Sawasa (alloy in %: copper: 94.4, gold: 1.9,
silver: 1.5, arsenic: 1.2, zinc: 0.1, lead: 0.05)
Height 18.5 cm. x diameter 14.0 cm.
Weight 800 gr.

A large circular tobacco jar with a
detachable lid. The lid has a tall finial in the
form of a double gourd. The jar consists of
an inner gilt layer and an outer layer of
black lacquered open relief scrolling foliage,
interspersed with gilt flowers and
karashishi. The inside of the jar, which is
gilded, has a second gilt lid.

B.20.2

Large circular jar

Private collection
Sawasa
6.5 x 12.6 cm.
555 gr.

A large circular jar with a detachable lid.
The lid and bottom have circular
cartouches decorated with pavilions and
figures in a boat in a traditional Chinese
landscape setting with trees and birds.
The sides are not decorated but have two
gilt profiled rims. The lid consists of high
and flat gilt relief decoration on a gilt
granulated background; the bottom has
only flat relief decoration. The inside is
gilded and shows indentations on the
bottom.

B.20.3

Circular canister

Private collection
Sawasa
6.6 x 9.6 cm.
380 gr.

A large circular canister with a detachable
lid. The sides of the lid fully cover the sides
of the body when closed. The top and
sides of the lid have cartouches decorated
with black lacquered relief designs on a
gilt granulated background. The
decoration includes pavilions, a figure in a
boat and two goats in a traditional
Chinese landscape setting with trees and
birds. The remaining surfaces around the
sides are engraved and gilt with peony
scrolls. The outside of the body is black
lacquered with a gilt rim and has no
decoration. The inside is entirely gilded.

B.20.4

Circular comfit box

Private collection
Sawasa
3.8 x 3.9 cm.
118 gr.

A circular comfit box with a detachable lid. The box is shaped from Sawasa plate. The lid is decorated in European style with rococo ornaments and foliage depicting a female figure holding a parasol and sitting in a chariot drawn by dogs. The inside is gilded.

B.20.5

Small circular box with a threaded lid

Private collection
Sawasa
3.2 x 6.0 cm
120 gr.

A small circular box with a threaded lid. The thread has been attached to the inside of the body and lid by gilt rivets. The top panel of the lid is decorated in black lacquered relief designs on a gilt granulated background with trees, pavilions and birds in a traditional Chinese landscape setting. The sides of the lid and body have continuous decoration of squirrels with nuts or grapes and scrolling foliage. The inside is partly gilded.

.20.6

Large rectangular tobacco jar

Private collection
Sawasa
Height 16.4 cm. x length 12.8 cm. x
width 12.8 cm.
Weight 930 gr.

A large rectangular tobacco jar with a detachable pyramidal lid. On top of the lid is a gilt snake with a barbed tail, its body twisted to form a handle. The jar consists of an inner gilt layer and an outer layer of black lacquered open relief patterns, with gilt panels decorated with open worked geometrical forms. The jar stands on four gilt rounded feet and has gilt profiled rims around the sides. The inside of the jar, which is gilded, has a second gilt lid and shows bronze-coloured metal where it is worn.

The Catalogue

Pipe cases were used to carry European clay-pipes. It seems pipe-cases were rare in the seventeenth and eighteenth centuries and were only used by a small elite for travelling or for preserving a favourite pipe. Only a few pipe-cases still exist in museum collections, all made of expensive materials. Normally, Europeans would not take such precautions for safeguarding their pipes. Clay-pipes were cheap and would break very easily. It was not surprising that men used them in large quantities. Therefore, the main motive for having such an expensive utensil, unsuited for any other purpose, would have been for the display of wealth. The pipe-cases in this catalogue have a combination of Sawasa with shark skin, as is the case with the scabbards and the cane. The pipe-cases can be dated

Sawasa Tobacco- and Betel-Equipment

quite strictly between 1680 and 1720. During this period, pipes of forty to fifty centimetres were fashionable, a length fitting these cases. After 1720 pipes first became longer and later much shorter.

Betel-boxes contained utensils and ingredients to make a quid for chewing. A betel-quid was the folded leaf of the Piper betel-tree, in the Dutch Asian settlements called sirih, smeared with lime on the inside. Folded inside the leaf was a slice of areca-nut (pinang in Malay) with gambir-gum. The box contained a leaf-holder, boxes for lime, pinang and gambir, a betel-nut cutter and a pin to smear the lime on the leaf. Pinang has a slightly intoxicating effect and colours red when chewed. Betel-chewing was common in Asia long before Europeans arrived there. When Europeans mixed with Asians, the habit became part of the Eurasian household. European men took to the habit in the seventeenth century, although they kept smoking their pipes, too. From circa 1750 betel-chewing seemed exclusively a women's affair. Wealthy Eurasian ladies in Batavia and other Dutch settlements in Asia had a special woman slave to carry the betel-box wherever they went. In Eurasian culture the appearance and decoration of the betel-box had both European and Asian elements, as is the case with the box in this catalogue. When sirih-chewing became less fashionable among Eurasian families, especially the wealthier ones who owned these expensive boxes, the utensils were removed and betel-boxes were used for

keeping jewellery. A betel-box of tortoise-shell with Sawasa-mounts is described in a Batavia inventory of 1785 (Arsip Nasional Indonesia, Fam 581). Its owner was by Sophia Francina Westpalm, one of the richest ladies in the Dutch settlements in Asia and the widow of Governor-General Reinier de Klerk (1710-1780).

Kwispedoors or spittoons with a bulbous form and a wide extending mouth, as in this catalogue, are originally Asian and were used for the disposal of the betel quid. Like betel-boxes, spittoons became part of the Eurasian household, thus becoming subject to change in use and appearance. Small spittoons stood on tables, bigger ones on the floor. European men also used them to empty their pipes or to get rid of their tobacco-chew.

The *tabako-ire* is a Japanese combination of a tobacco-box and a pipe-case. In this catalogue we have an interesting Euro-Japanese one. The box is one of the early examples of Sawasa tobacco-boxes, of European form and Asian, presumably Japanese, manufacture and decoration. It is attached to a pipe case containing a pipe, both of Japanese design. After the Portuguese introduced tobacco in Japan, the Japanese began to design their own type of equipment. The rattan pipe case, called a *kiseruzutsu*, consisted of two overlapping shells. The short Japanese tobacco-pipes are called *kysaru* and are fitted with a small metal head. The question is who used this *tabako-ire*. As Europeans preferred to smoke larger pipes, the item seems, therefore, to have been made or remade for a Japanese customer.

M. de B.

Large rectangular betel (sirih) box of tortoise-shell

Private collection
Sawasa mounts
Height 9.0 cm. x length 21.0 cm. x
width 16.0 cm.
Weight 1165 gr.

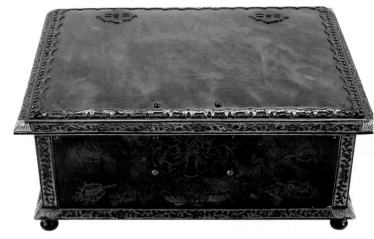

A large rectangular box of tortoise-shell with a hinged lid. There are two hinges attached to the box with screws, and a lock with a key. Around the keyhole is a black lacquered decorative panel depicting open relief scrolling foliage. The outer edges of the box are decorated with *shakudō* metal, which shows black lacquered relief floral scrolling on a gilt granulated background. The lid has an elaborate engraved armorial showing a Japanese man and woman and a table with smoking equipment. The sides show engraved flower arrangements. The box stands on four black lacquered metal feet, of which two have been replaced. The back of the hinges and lock, and the inside of the bottom are gilded.

Oval tobacco box with attached pipe case (tabako-ire)

Private collection
Sawasa
Box: 2.9 x 8.5 x 7.1 cm.
Pipe case: length 21.2 cm. x
width 19.6 cm.
178 gr.

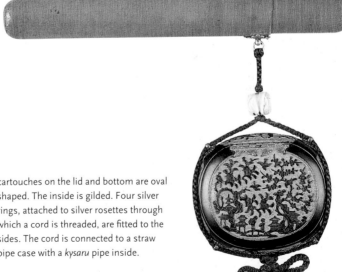

An oval shaped tobacco box with a hinged lid and curved convex sides. The lid, bottom and sides depict traditional Chinese landscape scenes with trees, pavilions, birds, horses and figures on a bridge in black lacquered relief designs on a gilt granulated background. The cartouches on the lid and bottom are oval shaped. The inside is gilded. Four silver rings, attached to silver rosettes through which a cord is threaded, are fitted to the sides. The cord is connected to a straw pipe case with a *kysaru* pipe inside.

C.3.1

Pipe case

Private collection
Sawasa mounts
53.5 x 5.0 cm.
214 gr.

A large double pipe case made of wood covered in shark skin with black lacquered patterns. The pipe case has a hinged lid nailed to the outside and opens by means of a switch button. The Sawasa hinge and clasp are decorated with black lacquered relief peonies, birds and a butterfly on a gilt granulated background. On the bottom of the case is a gilt mount, decorated with black lacquered relief trees, pavilions and birds.

C.3.2

Pipe case

Private collection
Sawasa mounts
44.0 x 5.5 cm.
224 gr.

A large double pipe case made of wood covered in shark skin with black lacquered patterns. The pipe case has a hinged lid nailed to the outside and opens by means of a switch button. The Sawasa hinge and clasp are decorated with black lacquered relief trees and birds on a gilt granulated background. On the bottom of the case is a gilt mount, decorated with black lacquered relief trees and birds.

C.4.1

Spittoon

Rijksmuseum Amsterdam, The Netherlands
Inv. No. NG-1994-37-B (CNO-111-B)
Height 12.4 cm. x diameter 14.9 cm.
Weight 570 gr.

A spittoon consisting of a gilt foot and trumpet-shaped mouth and a black lacquered bulbous body. The body is decorated with three lobed cartouches in high gilt relief designs on a gilt granulated background, depicting pavilions and a figure in a boat in a traditional Chinese landscape setting with trees and birds. The middle of the body shows gilt engraved fretwork. The inside of the mouth is gilded and engraved with peonies, butterflies and a bird.

C.4.2

Spittoon

Rijksmuseum Amsterdam, The Netherlands
Inv. No. NG-1994-37-C (CNO-111-C)
13.1 x 14.5 cm.
595 gr.

A spittoon consisting of a gilt foot and trumpet-shaped mouth and a black lacquered bulbous body. The body is decorated with three lobed cartouches in high gilt relief designs on a gilt granulated background, depicting pavilions and figures in a boat in a traditional Chinese landscape setting with trees, birds and a butterfly. The middle of the body shows gilt engraved fretwork. The inside of the mouth is gilded and engraved with fruits, flowers and birds.

The Catalogue

Sawasa Drinking Utensils

Through global trade in the seventeenth century, Europe came to know three exotic beverages: coffee, tea and chocolate. In the beginning, the enjoyment of these beverages was restricted to the upper classes, but towards the end of the eighteenth century, tea and coffee became popular among all classes. Because of the high price of cocoa, chocolate remained a drink for the elite for a long time. With the introduction of these new beverages, utensils for drinking were needed, especially in the eighteenth century when drinking tea, coffee and chocolate became an almost ceremonial happening.

Along with the new beverages, pots were imported from Asia to prepare the drinks. In many cases existing pots, which traditionally had been in use for other purposes, were given a new function. Both the small spherical pots made of red pottery or porcelain, later of Sawasa, used in China for wine or brandy, as well as the

Sawasa Drinking Utensils

larger pots that were probably used for boiling water, were used for tea by Europeans.

The first coffeepots in Europe were of Arabic origin, like the coffee itself. Their shape was derived from the Persian winepot and they had a slender neck, spout and handle with a bulbous body. For a long time these Persian pots had been made of porcelain in China and Japan for the Arabic market, but since the late seventeenth century, Sawasa pots were also exported to Persia and the Middle East. Soon these pots were to be sold in Europe as well. Perhaps the first indigenous European design for a coffee pot was a conical pot with a handle and spout, which soon evolved into an urn with taps. Initially, these urns had a conical shape, three feet and one or three taps. These different kinds of urns were produced in Japan; first made of porcelain, later of Sawasa. Note that these urns were also used for tea and chocolate.

The first cups for tea or coffee in Europe, exported from China and Japan, were small bowls with a saucer, into which the hot liquid was poured and from which it was drunk. From the second half of the eighteenth century, the cups were given handles and the saucers, which were still used as drinking bowls, gained a raised rim at the centre. The cups became quite wide with low spherical sides. This model became particularly popular for Sawasa, most probably for use as coffee or tea cups and perhaps also for wine or brandy. During the eighteenth century, drinking utensils became more luxurious and were made as complete sets, including bowls for sugar and comfits, and small stoves to heat the water.

In this catalogue Sawasa pots are called ewers for it is not known whether they were used for hot water, tea, coffee, chocolate, wine or brandy.

Q.L.

Urn

Private collection
Sawasa
Height 32 cm. x width 27.3 cm. x diameter
17.2 cm.
Weight 1990 gr.

A large urn with three gilt legs stemming from a *karashishi*-head and ending in a claw, three gilt spouts in the shape of dragon-heads with stoppers in the form of mythical fish and two gilt handles in the shape of branches with gilt sculptured blossom twisted around the body. The body consists of a bulbous lower part and a conical upper part, soldered together.

They are decorated with four cartouches in high black lacquered relief designs on a gilt granulated background depicting traditional Chinese landscape scenes with trees, pavilions, birds, butterflies and figures. The remaining surfaces on the body are engraved and gilt with peony scrolls and lotus borders on a black lacquered background. On top is a

detachable domed lid in three stages with a small finial, decorated with black lacquered relief birds and trees on a gilt granulated background. Apart from the legs and handles, which are bolted to the body, all the parts are soldered together. The inside is gilded over a layer of red lacquer.

Urn

Private collection
Sawasa (alloy in %: copper: 94.8, silver:
2.2, zinc: 1.0, arsenic: 0.7, gold: 0.6, nickel:
0.2, tin: 0.2, lead: 0.1, chromium: 0.05)
35.8 x 22.1 x 16.4 cm.
1988 gr.

A large urn with three gilt legs stemming from a *karashishi*-head, three gilt taps with stoppers in the form of mythical fish and two gilt handles with gilt sculptured foliage twisted around the body. The body consists of a black lacquered bulbous lower part and a gilt conical upper part. They are decorated with five cartouches in high black lacquered relief designs on a gilt granulated background, depicting traditional Chinese landscape scenes with trees, pavilions, birds and figures in a boat. The remaining surfaces on the body are engraved and gilt with scrolling foliage, fretwork and lotus borders. On top is a detachable domed lid with gilt engraved foliage scrolls and lotus borders on a black lacquered background. The lid has a gilt finial in the form of a twig. Apart from the handles and the finial, which are riveted to the urn, all the parts are soldered together. The inside of the lid is gilded.

Globular shaped pot

Private collection
Sawasa
Height 10.1 cm. x width 13.7 cm.
330 gr.

A small globular shaped pot with a gilt handle,
spout and base soldered to a black lacquered
body. On either side of the body is a lobed
cartouche decorated in high black lacquered relief
designs on a gilt granulated background,
depicting pavilions and a boat in a traditional
Chinese landscape setting with trees and birds.
On top is a detachable black lacquered lid with an
engraved gilt rim and a gilt finial in the form of a
sculptured twig with black lacquered blossom. The
inside is gilded.

Six-lobed pot

Private collection
Sawasa
13.1 x 15.8 cm.
360 gr.

A black lacquered six-lobed pot with a gilt handle, a gilt
spout in the form of a bamboo stem and an engraved
gilt neck. On either side of the body are two lobed
cartouches decorated in high black lacquered relief
designs on a gilt granulated background, depicting
trees, pavilions and birds in a traditional Chinese
landscape setting. The panels on which the handle is
nailed and the spout is soldered, have gilt engraved
foliage scrolling. The bottom is gilded and the lid is
missing.

Six-lobed pot

Private collection
Sawasa
17.8 x 18.8 cm.
610 gr.

A black lacquered six-lobed pot with a gilt handle in the form of a branch, a gilt spout which resembles a bamboo stem from which originate two shoots and an engraved gilt neck. On either side of the body are two lobed cartouches, decorated with gilt relief designs on a gilt granulated background depicting trees, flowers, butterflies and boats. The bottom is gilded. On top is a gilt lid with engraved foliage decoration and a later red stone knob, attached a-centrally on the gilded inside of the lid by a small gilt rosette.

Ewer

Private collection
Sawasa
21.0 x 11.9 cm.
496 gr.

A gilt ewer with a four-lobed bulbous body, a slender neck, a curved slender spout and handle, and a foot in the shape of lotus leaves, all soldered to the body. The hollow lid is attached to the handle by a chain and has a finial in the shape of a *karashishi*. The neck, body and foot are decorated with engraved foliage scrolls. The spout stems from an engraved monster-head. On either side of the body is a lobed cartouche surrounded by two brown lacquered borders, with high gilt relief trees and birds on a gilt granulated background. The handle ends in a lobed cartouche decorated with gilt relief pine trees.

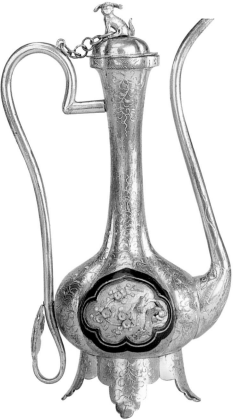

Ewer

Private collection
Sawasa
30.0 x 16.2 cm.
1050 gr.

A black lacquered ewer with a bulbous body, a slender neck, a curved slender spout and handle, a gilt foot and a gilt lid with a finial in the shape of a *karashishi*. The solid lid is attached to the handle by a chain. The foot is soldered to the foot ring and has a single central rivet decorated with a rosette. The lid, neck and body are engraved and gilt with peony and other foliage scrolls, the foot with a lotus border. The spout stems from a gilt base in the shape of a monster-head and has a gilt top. On either side of the body is a lobed cartouche, decorated in high gilt relief designs on a gilt granulated background with trees, birds, a butterfly and a *karashishi*. The handle ends in a gilt lobed cartouche with a peony. On the body are some old repairs showing cracks.

Ewer

Private collection
Sawasa
18.2 x 10.8 cm.
1150 gr.

A black lacquered ewer of hexagonal form with a bulbous body and a slender neck. The solid foot is attached to the body with a single rivet, and the curved slender spout and handle are gilt. The lid has a gilt finial in the shape of a *karashishi*, screwed on top, and is attached to the handle by a chain. The ewer has gilt engraved decoration of lotus borders and fretwork scrolls on the neck and body and floral scrolling on the lid and foot. The spout and handle stem from monster-heads. The handle ends on one side in a lobed cartouche decorated with a gilt relief plum tree on a gilt granulated background and on the other side in a dragon-head attached to the body with a split pin. Each of the six sides of the body has a lobed cartouche decorated with high gilt relief landscape scenes with trees, pavilions, birds and figures.

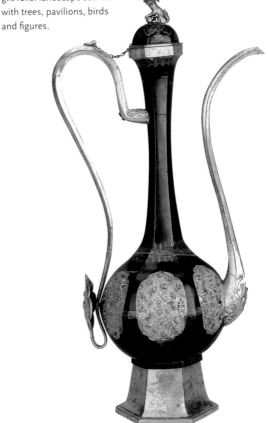

Ewer

Private collection
Sawasa
24.9 x 16.9 cm.
560 gr.

A gilt ewer with a bulbous body, a slender neck, a curved slender spout and handle and a foot in the shape of four lotus leaves standing on a ring. The foot is attached to the body with a bolt. The lid has a finial in the shape of a *karashishi*, riveted on top. The chain that attaches the lid to the handle is missing. The lid, neck, body and foot are decorated with engraved foliage scrolls. The spout stems from an engraved monster-head. On either side of the body is a lobed cartouche surrounded by a prominent gilt border which is a separate appliqué with high gilt relief trees and birds on a gilt granulated background. The handle ends in a lobed cartouche decorated with gilt relief pine trees. This ewer forms a similar but not identical pair with D.3.5.

Ewer

Private collection
Sawasa
25.4 x 17.2 cm.
575 gr.

A gilt ewer with a bulbous body, a slender neck, a curved slender spout and handle, and a foot in the shape of four lotus leaves standing on a ring. The foot is attached to the body with a bolt. The lid has a finial in the shape of a *karashishi*, riveted on top. The chain that attaches the lid to the handle is missing. The lid, neck, body and foot are decorated with engraved foliage scrolls. The spout stems from an engraved monster-head. On either side of the body is a lobed cartouche, surrounded by a prominent gilt border which is a separate appliqué, depicting high gilt relief trees and birds on a gilt granulated background. The handle ends in a lobed cartouche, decorated with gilt relief pine trees. This ewer forms a similar but not identical pair with D.3.4.

Cup and saucer

Rijksmuseum Amsterdam, The Netherlands
Inv. No. NG-1994-37-I/E (CNO-111-I/E)
Sawasa
Cup: 3.2 x 9.5 cm.
*   119 gr.*
Saucer: 0.9 x 12.6 cm.
*   186 gr.*

A black lacquered cup with gilt handles in the shape of sculptured chrysanthemums and a lobed edge decorated with a gilt engraved lotus border. The cup has a gilt foot that fits into the saucer ring and has two lobed cartouches showing gilt relief trees and birds on a gilt granulated background.

A gilt saucer with a black lacquered bracket-lobed edge, depicting gilt engraved peony scrolls, and three lobed cartouches decorated with high gilt relief trees and birds on a gilt granulated background. The centre of the saucer shows an engraved chrysanthemum, enclosed by a raised ring upon which the cup fits. Between this ring and the outer border is a circular panel decorated with high gilt relief trees, flowers, birds and a butterfly on a gilt granulated background, contained within a black lacquered border with a gilt engraved lotus decoration. The bottom is entirely gilded.

Cup and saucer,

Japan, 1731

The Metropolitan Museum of Art,
New York, USA
Acc. No. 1984.233a/b
Sawasa
Diameter cup: 7,6 cm.
Diameter saucer: 11.7 cm.
Height: 3.8 cm.
198 gr.

A black lacquered cup with two gilt handles in the shape of sculptured foliage and a lobed edge, decorated with a gilt engraved lotus border. The cup has a gilt foot that fits into the saucer ring and has two bracket-lobed cartouches, depicting black lacquered relief birds, flowers and foliage on a gilt granulated background. The inside is gilded. A gilt saucer with a lobed edge and black lacquered relief decorations of trees and birds on a gilt granulated background, surrounded by a black lacquered outline. The centre of the saucer shows an engraved chrysanthemum enclosed by a raised ring upon which the cup fits. Between this ring and the outer border is a circular panel decorated with high black lacquered relief trees, pavilions and birds on a gilt granulated background, contained within a black lacquered border with a gilt engraved lotus decoration. The bottom is entirely gilt and has an engraved inscription, 'IAPAN.ANNO.1731'.

Large cup with lid,

c.1750

Peabody Essex Museum, Salem, Mass., USA
Cat. No. E84 102AB
Sawasa
15.5 x 8.8 cm.
409 gr.

A black lacquered U-shaped cup, the sides flaring from the domed foot, with a shallow lid topped with a finial in the form of a double gourd. Around the sides are two oval gilt cartouches on a black lacquered granulated background, each with a somewhat fanciful rendering of the coat of arms and armorial shield of the Boonen family. The armorial shield shows three beanstalks on a field of grass; the literal interpretation of the family name Boonen (beans). The Boonen family were wealthy timber merchants in Dordrecht during the seventeenth and eighteenth centuries. The remaining surfaces on the sides, lid and foot are engraved and gilt with lotus decoration. The inside is gilded.

Sake cup

Private collection
Sawasa
3.0 x 5.8 cm.
57 gr.

A black lacquered cup with a gilt foot. The edge is engraved and gilt with a lotus border. The sides are decorated with three lobed cartouches depicting high gilt relief trees, fruits and birds on a gilt granulated background. The inside and bottom are gilded. This cup forms a similar but not identical pair with D.5.2b.

Sake cup

Private collection
Sawasa
3.0 x 5.7 cm.
53 gr.

A black lacquered cup with a gilt foot. The edge is engraved and gilt with a lotus border. The sides are decorated with three lobed cartouches depicting high gilt relief fruits, flowers and birds on a gilt granulated background. The inside and bottom are gilded. The cup forms a similar but not identical pair with D.5.2a.

Cup

Private collection
Sawasa
3.5 x 8.0 cm.
69 gr.

A black lacquered cup with a gilt foot and two gilt handles showing *mokume* sides and a gilt relief flower decoration on top. The edge of the cup is engraved and gilt with a lotus border. The sides have lobed cartouches, decorated with high gilt relief trees and birds on a gilt granulated background. The rough inside and bottom are gilded.

Cup

Private collection
Sawasa
3.9 x 5.3 cm.
64 gr.

A black lacquered U-shaped cup decorated
with three lobed cartouches in high black
lacquered relief designs on a gilt granulated
background. The decoration depicts trees,
birds and a figure in a boat contained
within a black lacquered border. The inside
gilding is worn. This cup forms a similar
but not identical pair with D.5.4b.

Cup

Private collection
Sawasa
3.9 x 5.2 cm.
67 gr.

A black lacquered U-shaped cup decorated
with three lobed cartouches in high black
lacquered relief designs on a gilt granulated
background. The decoration depicts trees,
birds and a figure in a boat, contained
within a black lacquered border. The inside
gilding is heavily worn. This cup forms a
similar but not identical pair with D.5.4a.

Saucer

Private collection
Sawasa
1.1 x 13.5 cm.
198 gr.

A saucer with a bracket-lobed edge, showing
mokume decoration at the centre panel and the
middle circular border. The inner border and
edge are gilt and have high relief decoration
depicting trees, pavilions, birds, figures in a
boat, flowers, nuts or grapes and a squirrel on a
granulated background. A raised ring of black
lacquer, upon which a cup fits, encloses the
centre panel. The bottom is gilded and shows
chatter marks and signs of wear.

D.6.2

Saucer

Private collection
Sawasa
1.0 x 14.3 cm.
194 gr.

A gilt saucer with a black lacquered
bracket-lobed edge, with gilt engraved
peony scrolls and four lobed cartouches
decorated with high gilt relief plants,
flowers and birds on a gilt granulated
background. The centre of the saucer has
a black lacquered circular panel decorated
with gilt engraved peony scrolls. Between
this panel and the outer border is a
circular panel decorated with high gilt
relief trees, birds and a butterfly on a gilt
granulated background. The panel is
contained within a gilt border with an
engraved lotus decoration, followed by a
plain gilt border. The bottom of the saucer
is gilded and shows chatter marks and
signs of wear.

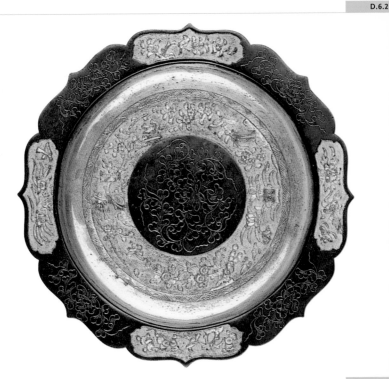

D.6.3a

Saucer

Private collection
Sawasa
1.2 x 9.6 cm.
118 gr.

A black lacquered saucer with a gilt foot
ring. The centre has a black lacquered and
gilt engraved chrysanthemum,
surrounded by a circular border decorated
with black lacquered relief trees, flowers,
pavilions and birds on a gilt granulated
background, contained within a black
lacquered frame. Two other borders depict
an engraved fishroe and crosses pattern.
The bottom is gilded and has an imprint in
the form of a cross over a central
punchmark. On the surface of the bottom
are concentric marks caused by it being
worked on a lathe. The saucer is similar
but not identical to D.6.3b.

Saucer

Private collection
Sawasa
1.2 x 9.6 cm.
113 gr.

A black lacquered saucer with a gilt foot
ring. The centre has a black lacquered and
gilt engraved chrysanthemum, surrounded
by a circular border decorated with black
lacquered relief trees, flowers, birds and a
butterfly on a gilt granulated background,
contained within a black lacquered frame.
Two other borders depict an engraved
fishroe and crosses pattern. The bottom is
gilded and has an imprint in the form of a
cross over a central punchmark. On the
surfaces of the bottom are concentric
marks caused by it being worked on a lathe.
The saucer is similar but not identical to
D.6.3a.

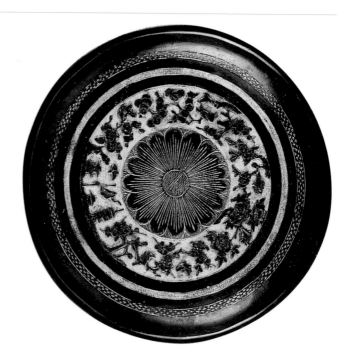

Saucer

Private collection
Sawasa
1.4 x 10.6 cm.
144 gr.

A black lacquered saucer with a gilt foot
ring. The centre has a gilt engraved
chrysanthemum, surrounded by a circular
border decorated with black lacquered relief
trees, a pavilion and birds on a gilt
granulated background, contained within a
black lacquered frame. In the centre of the
chrysanthemum is a punchmark. There is
another border showing a gilt engraved
lotus decoration. The bottom is gilded. This
saucer is similar but not identical to D.6.4b.

Saucer

Private collection
Sawasa
1.4 x 10.6 cm.
139 gr.

A black lacquered saucer with a gilt foot
ring. The centre has a gilt engraved
chrysanthemum, surrounded by a circular
border decorated with black lacquered
relief trees, pavilions, birds and fruits on a
gilt granulated background, contained
within a black lacquered frame. In the
centre of the chrysanthemum is a
punchmark. There is another border
showing a gilt engraved lotus decoration.
The bottom is gilded. This saucer is
similar but not identical to D.6.4.a.

Saucer

Private collection
Sawasa (alloy in %: copper: 96.7, silver:
1.0, zinc: 0.7, gold: 0.6, arsenic: 0.5, tin:
0.1, nickel: 0.1, lead: 0.09, chromium:
0.07)
1.4 x 10.3 cm.
112 gr.

A black lacquered saucer with a gilt foot
ring. The centre has a gilt engraved flower
decoration, enclosed by a lotus border.
There is another border with high gilt relief
decoration depicting trees, pavilions, birds
and a figure in a boat on a gilt granulated
background. In the centre of the bottom is
a punchmark and on the sides are chatter
marks. The bottom is gilded and shows
indentations.

Sugar bowl

Rijksmuseum Amsterdam,
The Netherlands
Inv. No. NG-1994-37-D (CNO-111-D)
Sawasa
5.8 x 13.3 cm.
378 gr.

A black lacquered semi-circular
sugar bowl which stands on a
black lacquered ring with a gilt
inside. The sides are decorated
with three lobed cartouches in high
gilt relief designs on a gilt granulated
background, depicting pavilions and a
figure in a boat in a traditional Chinese
landscape setting with trees and birds.
The rim around the edge is decorated
with a gilt engraved lotus border. The
inside is gilded and shows
indentations, proving that it was
chased after casting. The thick layer of
black lacquer shows signs of repairs.

Vessel

Private collection
Sawasa
4.5 x 7.9 cm.
388 gr.

A vessel with a bulbous body, a slender
neck with *mokume* decoration and a foot
ring. The body is decorated with gilt
engraved foliage and peony scrolls. On
either side is a bracket-lobed cartouche,
with high gilt relief trees, pavilions, birds,
figures and a *karashishi* on a gilt granulated
background. A plain black lacquered area
without engraving shows the original
position of a handle.

The Catalogue

Incense was first used in China as a form of fumigation. It was used to combat insect pests, while at the same time being totally harmless and giving out a pleasant odour. As early as the Zhou period (1027-221BC) artemisia was burned, its dense clouds of fragrant smoke also serving to mask unpleasant smells. Both vegetable and animal incenses were used. The plant incenses included cassia, camphor, liquorice and fennel, while the animal kingdom supplied such perfumes as civet and musk. From the seventh century onwards, imported fragrances such as sandalwood, garuwood, ambergris and gum benzoin supplemented the indigenous incense perfumes. The incense came in the form of powder or cones, which were embedded in a layer of sand or ash in a censer base. For daily use in scenting the home or in offering homage to household deities, however, incense sticks were traditionally used. They were held in incense stick holders, of which we have some examples in this catalogue. By the tenth century, a wide range of censers and containers were available.

crowns the domed openworked lids. Openwork covers not only created interesting patterns in the rising smoke, but also afforded a measure of protection from fire by preventing exploding embers from bursting out of the censer. The censers probably date from about the mid-eighteenth century when the use of covers increased dramatically.

From the third century onwards the Chinese created specialised incense burners. Such censers usually had a cup-like container with a perforated conical cover in the form of a mountain peak, set on top of a slender tubular stalk, secured in a small saucer-like basin. Smoke from the burning incense in the container was able to emerge through the perforations in the cover. Water in the basin not only afforded a measure of protection against fire, but also completed the mountain-water symbolism emblematic of all nature, of *yin* and *yang*, of female and male. With the rise of Buddhism during the centuries that followed, two new types of censers appeared for use in Buddhist ceremonies. One type, which had a circular, bowl-shaped container and a long straight handle, was carried in processions. The other type, which was for use on altars, had a circular, basin-like container that was surmounted by a tall, pierced, domed cover on top of a ring with usually five legs in the form of lion's claws.
The tenth century witnessed the introduction of another censer shape: a vessel with a deep cup-like container resting on a flaring pedestal base and with a wide horizontal rim at the mouth. In the following centuries several variations on that shape evolved. The six-lobed covered Sawasa censers in this catalogue descend from the so-called

The circular covered Sawasa boxes in our catalogue, that were used for the storage of powdered incense, are derived from the bronze incense boxes that became fashionable in the late sixteenth and early seventeenth centuries. They trace their lineage through the small jade and lacquer boxes of the fourteenth and fifteenth centuries, to the covered ceramic boxes dating from the tenth to the thirteenth centuries, and ultimately to the gold and silver boxes that enjoyed popularity in aristocratic circles during the seventh to the ninth centuries. Their short footring, low-set proportions and slightly domed cover link them to Qianlong-period jade examples, placing them firmly in the eighteenth century.

R.K.

Censer with openwork cover

Private collection
Sawasa
Height 10.4 cm. x diameter 10.0 cm.
Weight 560 gr.

A black lacquered censer with a six-lobed bulbous body, three gilt feet and a detachable gilt cover. The cover is domed and consists of open relief scrollwork with floral and foliage designs. On top is a small bead with a sculptured human face, attached to the cover by a cord. The mouth of the censer has a rim showing *mokume* decoration. Around the edge of the body is a knurled edged ring. Each of the six panels around the sides has a square-lobed cartouche, decorated with high gilt relief trees, flowers, birds and three Japanese figures on a gilt granulated background. On either side of the body is a gilt sculptured monster-head with a ring in its mouth. The inside is gilded and worn.

Censer with openwork cover

Private collection
Sawasa
13.4 x 11.4 cm.
580 gr.

A black lacquered censer with a six-lobed bulbous body, three gilt feet and a detachable gilt cover. The cover has a six-lobed edge and a domed section in the centre, consisting of open relief scrollwork with floral and foliage designs. On top is a gilt sculptured *karashishi*, riveted to the cover. The mouth of the body has a six-lobed rim with *mokume* decoration. Each of the six panels around the sides has a square-lobed cartouche decorated with high gilt relief trees, birds, three human figures at a tea ceremony, a Japanese figure on horseback and a figure waving a flag on a gilt granulated background. On either side of the body is a gilt sculptured monster-head. The rings in their mouths are missing. The inside is gilded.

Censer with openwork cover

Private collection
Sawasa
12.0 x 11.1 cm.
605 gr.

A black lacquered censer with a heavy six-lobed bulbous body, three feet with *mokume* decoration and a detachable gilt cover. The cover is domed and consists of open relief scrollwork with floral and foliage designs. On top is a gilt sculptured *karashishi*. The mouth of the censer has a rim showing *mokume* decoration. Each of the six panels around the sides has a square-lobed cartouche, decorated with high gilt relief trees, flowers and birds on a gilt granulated background. On either side of the body is a gilt sculptured monster-head with a ring in its mouth. The inside is gilded.

Censer with openwork cover

Private collection
Gilt bronze
12.3 x 9.0 cm.
505 gr.

A censer with a six-lobed bulbous body, three feet and a detachable domed cover, consisting of open relief floral and foliage scrollwork. On top is a small knob. Each of the six panels around the sides has a square-lobed cartouche, decorated with high gilt relief trees, flowers, birds and butterflies on a gilt granulated background. On either side of the body is a gilt sculptured monster-head with a ring in its mouth. The inside is gilded.

Large rectangular censer

Private collection
Sawasa
Height 27.0 cm. x length 22.5 cm.
x width 14.0 cm.
4440 gr.

A large rectangular black lacquered
censer with four gilt feet, two gilt
handles and a detachable gilt cover,
consisting of open relief scrollwork
interspersed with dragons. On top is a gilt
sculptured *karashishi*, riveted to the cover.
The mouth consists of a black lacquered
and gilt rim, engraved with foliage scrolls.
The edge of the body has a black
lacquered and a gilt knurled edged rim.
The sides have large square-lobed
cartouches, decorated with high gilt relief
trees, mythical animals, pavilions, figures
in a boat, cranes and other birds on a gilt
granulated background. The remaining
surfaces on the length of the rectangle and
the feet are engraved and gilt with foliage
scrolls. The gilt handles are decorated
with gilt engraved foliage scrolls and
cranes. The corners of the censer have
protruding gilt rims. The bottom and the
inside of the mouth are gilded.

Circular incense-stick holder

Private collection
Sawasa
Height 8.7 cm. x diameter 3.6 cm.
81 gr.

A small, narrow cylindrical incense-stick
holder with a gilt petalled neck and a gilt
domed foot riveted to the body. The body
is black lacquered and decorated with
three cartouches, with high gilt relief
peach, plum and pine branches on a gilt
granulated background.

Circular incense-stick holder

Private collection
Sawasa
10.4 x 3.5 cm.
152 gr.

A small, narrow, four-lobed incense-stick holder with a neck showing *mokume* decoration and a gilt circular stepped base with three feet. The body is black lacquered and decorated with four cartouches, containing high gilt relief trees, flowers and birds on a gilt granulated background.

Circular incense-stick holder

Private collection
Sawasa
10.3 x 3.2 cm.
131 gr.

A small, narrow four-lobed incense-stick holder with a gilt petalled neck and a gilt circular stepped base with four feet. The body is black lacquered and decorated with gilt engraved cartouches, showing landscape settings with trees, pavilions, birds, butterflies and Japanese figures. The neck is black lacquered and depicts fruits and flowers, done in the same technique.

Rectangular incense-stick holder

Private collection
Sawasa
Height 13.8 cm. x width 5.2 cm.
422 gr.

An incense-stick holder of widening square section with a gilt petalled neck and a gilt square-stepped base with four feet. The neck and base are engraved with flowers and geometrical patterns. The body has four black lacquered panels decorated with cartouches, depicting high gilt relief trees, flowers, a bird and a butterfly on a gilt granulated background.

Rectangular incense-stick holder

Private collection
Sawasa
9.4 cm. x 2.5 cm.
151 gr.

A small incense-stick holder of widening square section with a gilt petalled neck and a gilt square-stepped foot. The neck is engraved with floral decoration. The body has four black lacquered panels, decorated with cartouches, depicting high gilt relief trees, flowers and birds on a gilt granulated background.

Circular incense container

Private collection
Sawasa
Height 2.6 cm. x
diameter 6.0 cm.
106 gr.

A black lacquered circular box with a foot, a detachable lid and curved convex sides. The lid is decorated with a bracket-lobed cartouche depicting a squirrel with nuts or grapes in high gilt relief designs on a gilt granulated background. The sides are engraved and gilt with a double lotus border, fruits and flowers. The inside is gilded and shows signs of copper.

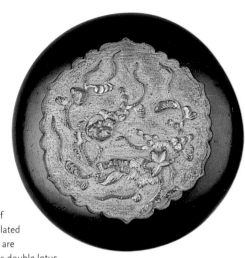

Circular incense container

Private collection
Sawasa
3.0 x 6.1 cm.
126 gr.

A black lacquered circular box with a foot, a detachable lid and curved convex sides. The lid is decorated with a bracket-lobed cartouche depicting a cherry tree, a pavilion and birds in high gilt relief designs on a gilt granulated background. The sides are engraved and gilt with a double lotus border, scrolling foliage and a mountain scene with a bird. The inside is gilded.

E.5.3

Circular incense container

Private collection
Sawasa
2.8 x 5.9 cm.
116 gr.

A black lacquered circular box with a foot, a
detachable lid and curved convex sides. The
lid is decorated with a bracket-lobed
cartouche depicting a rose bush and a
phoenix in high gilt relief designs on a gilt
granulated background. The sides are
engraved and gilt with a double lotus
border and have three lobed cartouches
depicting gilt relief trees, birds and a bee on
a gilt granulated background. The inside is
gilded.

E.5.4

Circular incense container

Private collection
Sawasa
3.1 x 6.2 cm.
128 gr.

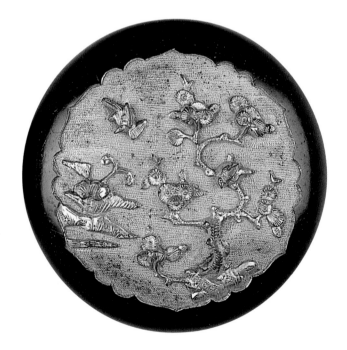

A black lacquered circular box with a foot, a
detachable lid and curved convex sides. The
lid is decorated with a bracket-lobed
cartouche depicting pine trees and birds in
high gilt relief designs on a gilt granulated
background. The sides are engraved and
gilt with a double lotus border, three
butterflies, a weeping willow and flowers.
The inside is gilded and shows signs of
copper with green efflorescence.

Circular incense container

Private collection
Sawasa
2.5 x 5.9 cm.
104 gr.

A black lacquered circular box with a foot,
a detachable lid and curved convex sides.
The lid is decorated with a bracket-lobed
cartouche depicting a plum tree and birds
in high gilt relief designs on a gilt
granulated background. The sides are
engraved and gilt with a double lotus
border, stylised birds and branches. The
inside is gilded and shows signs of
copper.

Circular incense container

Private collection
Sawasa
2.5 x 5.9 cm.
111 gr.

A black lacquered circular box with a foot,
a detachable lid and curved convex sides.
The lid is decorated with a bracket-lobed
cartouche depicting a plum tree and birds
in high gilt relief designs on a gilt
granulated background. The sides are
engraved and gilt with a double lotus
border, birds, fruits and flowers. The
inside is gilded and shows signs of copper
with green efflorescence.

Circular incense container

Private collection
Sawasa
2.6 x 6.1 cm.
104 gr.

A black lacquered circular box with a foot, a
detachable lid and curved convex sides. The
lid is decorated with a bracket-lobed
cartouche depicting a plum tree and a bird
in high gilt relief designs on a gilt
granulated background. The sides are
engraved and gilt with a double lotus
border, a bird, a butterfly and flowers. The
inside is gilded.

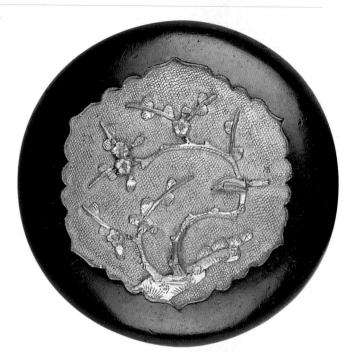

Circular incense container

Private collection
Sawasa (alloy in %: copper: 95.1, gold: 1.7,
silver: 1.4, arsenic: 0.9, zinc: 0.9, nickel:
0.17, lead: 0.15, chromium: 0.06, tin: 0.04)
3.2 x 6.5 cm.
122 gr.

A black lacquered circular box with a
mokume foot, a detachable lid and curved
convex sides. The box is decorated with gilt
engraved trees, pavilions, birds, Japanese
figures, a boat on the lid, and a double
lotus border, birds, fruits and flowers
around the sides. The inside is gilded.

The Catalogue

Sawasa accessories were made to order for Europeans in seventeenth and eighteenth century Asia. As Sawasa was very expensive, only the very wealthy could afford these accessories as part of their personal jewellery. Rich Europeans in Batavia would own at least one set of Sawasa buttons, sawasa buckles and some canes with Sawasa handles together with their silver and gold ones.

From eighteenth century written sources we know that many women's accessories were made of Sawasa or were decorated with Sawasa, such as combs, mounts of combs, rings and hairpins. There were also Sawasa accessories used by both sexes, such as chains for watches or boxes and korek koeping, a pin for cleaning ones ear. The accessories in this catalogue are exclusively made for men.

Chape-buckles were used in necktie-, shoe- and trouser-fastenings. We may assume that the men who wore them used matching sets of buckles on their clothing. The buckles in this catalogue have two hinged double pins and can be dated in the eighteenth century.

A European of some social standing in the seventeenth and eighteenth century never went out without his sword and cane. The cane handle was made of a decorated

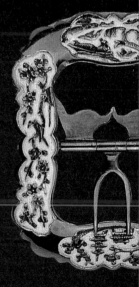

Sawasa accessories

precious metal and was a token of his high social status. In Asia, Europeans started using rattan for their canes. Like sword hilts with their scabbards, Sawasa cane handles sometimes were combined with ray skin or shark skin covering the cane. The conical cane handle, from which we have some examples, was used throughout the seventeenth and eighteenth centuries. From the pear-shaped handle we have only found seventeenth century models.

Sawasa buttons were bought in sets. The costume in this catalogue has twenty-one buttons on the frock coat, eighteen on the waistcoat. Written eighteenth century sources mention sets of forty-two buttons for a coat. For a camizool even a hundred are mentioned. Presumably, this was one regular set and one spare set. A camizool was a gentlemen's shirt with or without sleeves, thus ressembling a waistcoat, and was worn under a coat. Eighteenth century inventories also mention Sawasa

buttons for man's trousers. These were probably the short row of buttons just above the knee.

The Sawasa buttons in this catalogue can be dated between 1690 and 1800. From the end of the sixteenth century it was fashionable to have rows of buttons on man's suits. Hollow buttons made of precious metals were commonly used from the end of the seventeenth century. These consisted of two cast parts soldered together. Buttons similar to the large buttons on our coat, can be recognized in a portrait made in c. 1700 of Governor-General Willem van Outhoorn (1635-1720). According to the inventory of his possesions made after his death, he owned a 'chints costume with Tonkinese buttons'. (Rijksarchief Arnhem, archive Rosendael inv. nr. 781)

M. de B.

Coat with twenty-one buttons

Private collection
Sawasa buttons (alloy in %: copper: 93.6,
silver: 2.9, gold: 1.9, zinc: 0.7, arsenic:
0.5, nickel: 0.2, chromium: 0.1, lead:
0.08, tin: 0.08)
Diameter button 3.0 cm., length coat
100.0 cm.
Weight button 12 gr.

A hollow button of domed form made of
shakudô metal. The button is worked in
repoussé, depicting gilt relief trees, a
pavilion, birds and a rosette in the centre
on a dull black lacquered granulated
background. The back of the button is
patinated and has a loop to attach the
button to the fabric. The button belongs
to a gentleman's brown silk coat with
twenty-one similar buttons.

Waistcoat with eighteen buttons

Private collection
Sawasa buttons
Diameter button 1.8 cm.,
length coat 80.4 cm.

A hollow button of domed form made of
shakudô metal. The button is worked in
repoussé, showing gilt and black
lacquered flowers and foliage. In the
centre of the button is a gilt flower with a
tiny knob. The back is patinated and has a
loop to attach the button to the fabric.

Shoe/knee buckle

Private collection
Sawasa
Height 1.4 cm. x length 5.8 cm. x width 4.6 cm.
34 gr.

A black lacquered shoe or
knee buckle with a lobed
edge, decorated with four
lobed cartouches
depicting black lacquered
relief trees, pavilions,
birds and a figure in a
boat on a gilt granulated
background.

F.2.1b

Shoe/knee buckle

Private collection
Sawasa
1.4 x 5.8 x 4.6 cm.
32 gr.

A black lacquered shoe or knee buckle with
a lobed edge, decorated with four lobed
cartouches depicting black lacquered relief
trees, pavilions, birds and a figure in a boat
on a gilt granulated background.

F.3.1

Walking cane handle

Private collection
Sawasa
Height 7.2 cm. x width 3.8 cm.
60 gr.

A walking cane handle, decorated
with three black lacquered open
relief panels, consisting of
continuous foliage scrolling,
interspersed with gilt squirrels
and nuts or grapes. The top is
decorated in the same technique
and shows gilt squirrels, nuts or
grapes and a rosette in the centre.
Above and below the panels are a
gilt rim and a gilt lotus border.

F.3.2

Walking cane handle

Private collection
Sawasa
12.0 x 4.3 cm.
115 gr.

A walking cane handle,
decorated with black lacquered
relief designs on a gilt
granulated background, with
trees, pavilions, figures, birds
and animals in a traditional
Chinese landscape setting.
The decoration is divided in
two halves by a gilt profiled rim
and black lacquered lotus
borders. On top of the handle
is a gilt and black lacquered
rosette. Around the bottom is
a black lacquered and a
second gilt rim with an
engraved lotus decoration.

Walking cane

Private collection
Sawasa handle (alloy in %: copper: 98.5,
gold: 2.6, silver: 1.6, arsenic: 0.7, zinc: 0.6,
nickel: 0.2, lead: 0.07, tin: 0.07,
chromium: 0.06)
Handle: height 8.1 cm. x width 4.4 cm.
Handle and cane: weight 338 gr.

A walking cane handle, decorated with
black lacquered peony scrolls on a gilt
granulated background, separated by
gilt spiral bands. The top is decorated
in the same technique, with a lobed
cartouche depicting a phoenix and
foliage scrolls. Around the bottom are
two undecorated gilt rims. The handle
is affixed to a wooden walking cane.

Walking cane

Staatliche Kunstsammlungen Dresden,
Rüstkammer, Germany
Inv. No. 1505
Sawasa handle
Handle and cane: 104.8 cm.
Handle and cane: 200 gr.

The Sawasa handle is decorated with
black lacquered floral motives between
two different lotus borders. The cane is
pierced near the handle for a strap. This
piercing is decorated on both sides with
a gilt knurled edged ring. The rattan
cane is entirely covered with black
lacquered shark skin and ends with a
gilt copper cap.

Walking Cane

Private collection
Sawasa handle
Handle: 12.0 x 4.0 cm.
Handle and cane: 460 gr.

A walking cane handle decorated with black
lacquered relief designs on a gilt granulated
background, with trees, pavilions, birds,
deer and a figure in a boat. The top is
decorated in the same technique with a
lobed cartouche, depicting trees, pavilions
and birds. Around the bottom is a gilt ring,
enclosed by black lacquered and gilt lotus
borders. The handle has later been affixed
to the rattan stick of a blue umbrella.

Appendix 1

Peter Hallebeek

Methods of research

X-ray fluorescence spectrometry (nondestructive)

*X-ray diffraction
Microscopy*

FTIR (Fourier Transform Infrared Spectroscopy)

GC/MS (Gas Chromatography/Mass Spectrometry)

X-ray fluorescence spectrometry (RFS, EDX)

Using X-rays, this method makes it possible to detect elements and allows to determine the composition of inorganic materials such as metals, glass, stone, ceramics, etc, both qualitatively and quantitatively. The X-rays penetrate the surface, to a depth of 5-20 micron (0.005-0.02 mm). Only the composition of a thin superficial layer is thus determined and that only in an area of 2 mm². The primairy X-ray radiation provokes secundary radiation of specific wavelengths by which elements can be identified. The intensity of the secundary radiation is a measure for the quantity of the element present. The object under research is kept entirely outside the instrument at a distance of about 5 cm. The spot to be analysed on the surface is pinpointed by two intersecting laserbeams. The advantage of this method is its nondestructive nature, its disadvantage is that only the surface of the material is analysed.

X-ray diffraction

X-ray diffraction is a most useful analytical tool for solving problems with museum objects. Using reference data, more than 63.000 different, crystalline substances can be identified among which, minerals, metals, corrosion products, pigments, ceramic materials, clays, salt efflorescences and fillers in paints. Crystalline substances are composed of atoms arranged in a repeating three-dimensional pattern. The diffraction pattern of a substance can be considered the finger print of that particular material. Irradiation with X-rays makes the inner crystal planes reflect the radiation. By its specific geometry each crystalline substance has a specific reflection pattern. Luckily nearly all organic and inorganic compounds are crystalline with the exception among others of natural resins and glass. For the analysis a minute quantity of the substance is needed and this sample is not consumed.

Fourier Transform Infrared Spectroscopy

With the aid of an infrared spectometer chemical compounds can be identified through their different absorption spectra. Comparable with the X-ray diffraction method, unknown substances can be identified by comparing the spectrum with spectra of reference materials or by establishing the presence of specific functional groups of atoms in the molecule of the compound.

Gas Chromatography-Mass Spectrometry

The principle of mass spectrometry lies in the separation of organic compounds according to their molecular weights and polarity. The method can be used for the identification of organic materials such as fatty substances, resins, gums, glues etc. In mass spectrometry a small quantity of the material is brought into the apparatus; the components of the sample are partly fragmented (in a characteristic pattern) and ionised in an electron beam after which the ions are separated in a magnetic field according to their mass/charge ratio. In combination with gas chromatography the performance of the system is increased. (Riederer J., Archeologie und Chemie. Berlin 1987)

Appendix 2

Peter Hallebeek

*Results of analyses of a choice of
Sawasa objects*

*Characteristic main and secundary
elements in the metal alloys in
percentages of weight. The listed value is
the average value of three measurements
on different places on each object.
Accuracy of the measurements:
percentages lower than 5%: +/- 0,02%
percentages above 5%: +/- 0,50%*

Hanger (A.3.1)
Copper: 88.3
Zinc: 0.9
Lead: N D
Tin: 1.5
Chromium: 0.2
Nickel: 0.4
Cadmium: N D
Arsenic: 0.4
Silver: 3.5
Gold: 4.5

Hanger (A.1.1)
Copper: 95.8
Zinc: 0.9
Lead: 0.03
Tin: 1.6
Chromium: 0.1
Nickel: 0.2
Cadmium: N D
Arsenic: 0.2
Silver: 0.5
Gold: 0.7

Small-sword (A.9.3)
Copper: 95.8
Zinc: 0.9
Lead: 0.03
Tin: N D
Chromium: 0.1
Nickel: 0.1
Cadmium: N D
Arsenic: 0.7
Silver: 1.3
Gold: 1.0

Saucer (D.6.5)
Copper: 96.7
Zinc: 0.7
Lead: 0.09
Tin: 0.1
Chromium: 0.07
Nickel: 0.1
Cadmium: N D
Arsenic: 0.5
Silver: 1.0
Gold: 0.6

Ewer *(Not in
catalogue)*
Copper: 98.2
Zinc: 0.6
Lead: 0.4
Tin: N D
Chromium: 0.02
Nickel: 0.2
Cadmium: N D
Arsenic: 0.1
Silver: 0,07
Gold: 0.04

Urn (D.1.2)
Copper: 94.8
Zinc: 1.0
Lead: 0.1
Tin: 0.2
Chromium: 0.05
Nickel: 0.2
Cadmium: N D
Arsenic: 0.7
Silver: 2.2
Gold: 0.6

**Walking cane handle
(F.3.3)**
Copper: 98.5
Zinc: 0.6
Lead: 0.07
Tin: 0.07
Chromium: 0.06
Nickel: 0.2
Cadmium: N D
Arsenic: 0.7
Silver: 1.6
Gold: 2.6

Button (F.1.1)
Copper: 93.6
Zinc: 0.7
Lead: 0.08
Tin: 0.08
Chromium: 0.10
Nickel: 0.2
Cadmium: N D
Arsenic: 0.5
Silver: 2.9
Gold: 1.9

Tobacco jar (B.20.1)
Copper: 94.4
Zinc: 0.1
Lead: 0.05
Tin: N D
Chromium: N D
Nickel: N D
Cadmium: N D
Arsenic: 1.2
Silver: 1.5
Gold: 1.9

Tobacco box (B.17.3)
Copper: 94.0
Zinc: 0.7
Lead: 0.02
Tin: N D
Chromium: 0.08
Nickel: 0.2
Cadmium: N D
Arsenic: 0.4
Silver: 1.4
Gold: 1.9

Tobacco box (B.4.1)
Copper: 95.0
Zinc: 0.5
Lead: 0.1
Tin: 1.1
Chromium: 0.02
Nickel: 0.2
Cadmium: N D
Arsenic: 0.01
Silver: 0,3
Gold: 1.1

Tobacco box (B.7.1)
Copper: 95.6
Zinc: 0.5
Lead: 0.09
Tin: N D
Chromium: 0.05
Nickel: 0.2
Cadmium: N D
Arsenic: 0.7
Silver: 2.6
Gold: 0.2

Tobacco box (B.14.3)
Copper: 96.9
Zinc: 0.5
Lead: 0.1
Tin: 0.1
Chromium: 0.08
Nickel: 0.1
Cadmium: N D
Arsenic: 0.4
Silver: 1.5
Gold: 0.3

Tobacco box (B.1.3)
Copper: 92.8
Zinc: 0.7
Lead: 0.08
Tin: N D
Chromium: 0.04
Nickel: 0.2
Cadmium: N D
Arsenic: 1.0
Silver: 2.3
Gold: 2.7

**Book-shaped box
(B.19.2)**
Copper: 94.4
Zinc: 0.9
Lead: N D
Tin: N D
Chromium: 0.08
Nickel: 0.3
Cadmium: N D
Arsenic: 0.4
Silver: 2.6
Gold: 1.1

**Incense container
(E.5.8)**
Copper: 95.1
Zinc: 0.9
Lead: 0.15
Tin: 0.04
Chromium: 0.06
Nickel: 0.17
Cadmium: N D
Arsenic: 0.9
Silver: 1.4
Gold: 1.7

Notes

Introduction

1. R. Cederström, 'Japanska värjfästen i
   Europeiska 1700-talsformer', in: *Från Nordiska
   Museets samlingar bilder och studier tillägnade
   Gustaf Upmark på hans 50-årsdag den 13 Mars
   1925* (Stockholm, 1925)

2. C. Blair, *European and American Arms. c. 1100-
   1850* (London, 1962) 86 and Fig.153; Relatively
   unnoted, in 1976 the word suassa was
   introduced by J.B. Kist for a Sawasa coffee
   service, based on Rumphius: *Amboinsche
   Rariteit Kamer*, J.B. Kist, 'Een merkwaardig
   koffie servies', in: *Jaarverslagen 1974 en 1975
   van de Stichting Cultuurgeschiedenis
   Nederlanders Overzee*. (Amsterdam, 1976)

3. For instance: J.P. Puijpe, *The Visser Collection.
   Arms of the Netherlands in the collection of H.L.
   Visser*, Part 3 (Zwolle, 1996) 194-201, 238-239;
   A.V.B. Norman and C.M. Barne, *The rapier and
   the small sword 1460-1820* (London, 1980)

Chapter 1

1. For opposed views: H. Born, 'Multi-coloured
   Antique Bronze Statues', in: S. La Niece and
   P.T. Craddock (eds.), *Metal Plating and
   Patinating* (Oxford, 1993) 19-29, and P.T.
   Craddock, 'A Short History of the Patination of
   Bronze', in: M. Jones (ed.), *Why Fakes Matter*
   (London, 1992)

2. W.T. Chase and U.M. Franklin, 'Early Chinese
   Black Mirrors and Pattern-etched Weapons',
   Ars Orientalis 11 (Ann Arbor, 1979) 215-58

3. N.D. Meeks, 'Patination Phenomena on
   Roman and Chinese High-tin Bronze Mirrors
   and Other Artefacts', in: La Niece and
   Craddock, *Metal Plating and Patinating*, 63-84

4. Zhu Shoukang and He Tangkun, 'Studies of
   Ancient Chinese Mirrors and Other Bronze
   Artefacts', in: La Niece and Craddock, *Metal
   Plating and Patinating*, 50-62

5. M. Vickers, 'Artful Crafts: The Influence of
   Metalwork on Athenian Painted Pottery',
   Journal of Hellenic Studies 105 (London, 1985)
   108-128

6. For an effective demolition: J. Boardman,
   'Silver is White', *Revue Archeologique* 2 (Paris,
   1987) 279-285

7. P.T. Craddock and A. Giumlia Mair, '*Hśmn
   km*, Corinthian Bronze, *Shakudo*: Black-
   patinated Bronze in the Ancient World', in: La
   Niece and Craddock, *Metal Plating and
   Patinating*, 101-127, and P.T. Craddock and A.
   Giumlia Mair, 'The Identity of Corinthian
   Bronze: Rome's *Shakudo* Alloy', in: S.T.A.M.
   Mols (ed.) e.a., *Acta of the 12th International
   Congress on Ancient Bronzes* (Nijmegen, 1995)
   137-148

8. A. Giumlia Mair, 'Early Instances of *Shakudo*-
   type Alloys in the West', *Bulletin of the Japan
   Institute of Metals* 27 (1997) 3-16, and A.
   Giumlia Mair and S. Quirke, 'Black Copper in
   Bronze Age Egypt', *Revue d'Egyptologie* 48
   (Paris, 1997) 95-108

9. A. Giumlia Mair, 'Das Krokodil und
   Amenemhat III aus el-Faiyum', *Antike Welt.
   Zeitschrift fr Archäologie und Kulturgeschichte*
   1996, 4 (Mainz am Rhein, 1996) 313-322

10. Giumlia Mair and Quirke, 'Black Copper in
    Bronze Age Egypt', 95-108

11. A. Giumlia Mair, 'Das Sichelschwert von
    Bâlata-Sichem', *Antike Welt. Zeitschrift für
    Archäologie und Kulturgeschichte* 1996, 4
    (Mainz am Rhein, 1996) 340

12. J.D. Cooney, 'On the Meaning of Hsmn Km',
    *Zeitschrift für Ägyptische Sprache und
    Altertumskunde* 93 (Berlin, 1966) 43-47

13. J.D. Cooney, 'Siren and Ba: Birds of a Feather',
    Bulletin of the Cleveland Museum 55 (Cleveland,
    1968) 262-271

14. K.Demakopoulou e.a., 'Mycenaean Black
    Inlaid Metalware in the National Archeological
    Museum, Athens: A Technical Examination,
    Annual of the British School at Athens 90
    (Athens, 1996) 137-153

15. Giumlia Mair, 'Early Instances of *Shakudo*-type
    Alloys in the West', 3-16

16. H.L. Jones, *Pausanias: Description of Greece*. II
    (London, 1918) 261

17. R. Stillwell e.a., 'Corinth' 1.2, *Architecture*
    (Cambridge (Mass.), 1941)

18. H. Rackham, *Pliny: The Natural History*. III
    (London, 1940) 9.139, and H. Rackham, *Pliny:
    The National History*. IX (London, 1952) 34.1 &
    5-7

19. F.C. Babbitt, *Plutarch: Moralia*. V (London,
    1936) 395

20. Craddock and Giumlia Mair, '*Hśmn km*,
    Corinthain Bronze, *Shakudo*: black-patinated
    Bronze in the Ancient World', 101-107, and
    Craddock and Giumlia Mair, 'The Identity of
    Corinthian Bronze: Rome's *Shakudo* Alloy',
    137-148

21. Craddock and Giumlia Mair, '*Hśmn km*,
    Corinthain Bronze, *Shakudo*: black-patinated
    Bronze in the Ancient World', 101-107

22. W. Gowland, 'A Japanese pseudo-speiss,
    (shirome)', *Journal of the Society of Chemical
    Industry* 13 5 (Tokyo, 1894) 1-26, and W.C.
    Roberts-Austen, *Report on the Analysis of
    Various Examples of Oriental Metalwork in the
    South Kensington Museum*. (London, 1892),
    and S. La Niece, 'Japanese Polychrome
    Metalwork', in: E. Pernicka, e.a. (eds.),

Archaeometry '90 (Basel, 1990) 87-94

23. M. Berthelot, *La Chimie au Moyen Age. I-III*
    (Paris, 1893)

24. C. Stapleton e.a., 'Corinthium Aes and Black
    Bronze in the Early Medieval Period',
    Antiquaries Journal 75 (London, 1995) 383-90

25. J. Needham, *Sience and Civilisation in China*. 5
    (2) (Cambridge, 1974) 257-271

26. R.K. Dube, 'Some Literary and Documentary
    Evidences for Coloured Gold in Ancient India',
    *Bulletin of the Metals Museum of the Japan
    Institute of Metals*. 26 2 (1996) 27-32

27. A.C. Rây, *History of Chemistry in Ancient and
    Medieval India*. (Calcutta, 1956)

28. E. Lo Boe, 'Statuary Metals in Tibet and the
    Himalayas', in: W.A. Oddy, and W. Zwalf,
    'Aspects of Tibetan Metalwork', *British
    Museum Occasional Paper* 15 (London, 1981)
    33-67

29. G. Tucci, 'A Tibetan Classification of Buddhist
    Images According to Their Style', *Artibus Asiae*
    22 (Dresden, 1959)

30. R. Kerr, *Later Chinese Bronzes* (London, 1990)

31. P.T. Craddock, 'The Ancestors of Japanese
    Irogane', in: *Proceedings of the Forum for
    BUMA-IV* (Sendai, 1996) 79-84

32. H.B. Collier, 'Black Copper of Yunnan', *Journal
    of Chemical Education* 17 (Easton, 1940) 19-21

33. M. Wayman and P.T. Craddock, '*Wu Tong*, a
    Neglected Chinese Decorative Technology', in:
    La Niece and Craddock, *Metal Plating and
    Patinating*, 128-134

34. H.B. Collier, 'Black Copper of Yunnan', *Journal
    of Chemical Education* 17 (Easton, 1940) 19-21

35. A. Giumlia Mair and M. Lehr, 'Patinating Black
    Bronzes: Texts and Tests', in: *Proceedings of
    the BUMA IV Conference* (Matsue, 1998)

36. Mang Zidan and Han Rubin, 'Studies to the
    Blackening on Copper-silver-gold Alloy',
    Studies in the History of Natural Sciences 6 4
    –in Chinese- (1989)

Chapter 2

1. W.H. Medhurst, *An English and Japanese and
   Japanese and English Vocabulary. Compiled
   from Native Works* (Batavia, 1830) Kind
   information from Penelope Maskell.

2. J.F. Overmeer Fisscher, *Bijdrage tot de kennis
   van het Japansche rijk* (Amsterdam. 1833) 125-
   126.

3. Nihon daijiten kankokai (ed.),*Nihon kokugo
   daijiten* Vol. 9 (Tokyo, 1976) 188 (Japanese
   dictionary)

4. According to the Rev. Michael Cooper, S.J. in
   1973, letter to Claude Blair.

5. Municipal archives Delft, Familyrecords of van
   der Burch Inv. 141, last will of Dirk Graswinckel
   (1631-1697). 12 December 1695: '*de seer
   curieuse coper vergulde geemalieerde Japanse
   souatsche TabaxDoos mitsgaders de van boven
   en onder met Masijf goudt Draedwarck kunstigh
   Beslaghe Pijpekoker, mij door d'heer En Mr
   Willem van Oudhoorn generaal van India in den
   jaer 1695 vereert*'.

6. ARA, records of the Nederlandse Factorij
   Japan: Inv. 327, letter dated Nagasaki 29
   October 1696. All references to records of the

Nederlandse Factorij Japan, kindly communicated by Cynthia Viallee (University of Leiden).

7. Inventory of the estate of Joan van Hoorn, Batavia 1711, Municipal Archives Amsterdam, Inv. 5006, p. 735. Kind communication of Jan van Campen (University of Leiden).

8. G.E. Rumphius, *D'Amboinsche Rariteitkamer, behelzende eene beschrijving van allerhande zoo weeke als harde schaalvissen... alsmede allerhande hoorntjes en schulpen... benevens zommige mineraalen, gesteenten.* Book III, Part IV. (Amsterdam, 1741)
Mr. J.G. Huyser, 'Oud-Javaansche koper-legeeringen', in: *Cultureel Indië* I (Leiden, 1939) 227-231, 257-260, 292-297.

9. W.Ph. Coolhaas, J. van Goor (eds.), *Generale Missieven van Gouverneurs-Generaal en Raden aan Heren XVII der Verenigde Oostindische Compagnie,* dated 23 December 1644, Part II: *1639-1655.* (The Hague, 1960) 242, Rijks Geschiedkundige Publicatiën 112

10. An example of an Achinese kris with a black and gold decorated hilt, probably Sawasa, is in the National Museum of Indonesia, Jakarta, Inv. E.146 (Bataviaasch Genootschap No. 7858). See illustration.

11. ARA, records of the Nederlandse Factorij Japan: Inv.304, letter to Batavia 29 October 1673.

12. See for instance the sword furniture displayed in O. Kümmel, *Kunstgewerbe in Japan.* (Berlin, 1901) plate 90 and 95.

13. Dr. K. Herberts, *Das Buch der Ostasiatischen Lackkunst* (Dusseldorf, 1959) 376.

14. Two hilts, Cat. A 1.1 and A.1.2 and a tobacco box, Cat. B 4.1.

15. Municipal archives Delft, Family records of van der Burch Inv. 141, last will of Dirk Graswinckel (1631-1697). 12 December 1695: *'de seer curieuse coper vergulde geemalieerde Japanse souatsche TabakDoos mitsgaders de van boven en onder met Masijf goudt Draedwarck kunstigh Beslaghe Pijpekoker, mij door d'heer En Mr Willem van Oudhoorn generaal van India in den jaer 1695 vereert'.*

16. Even more exemplary is that Graswinckel's descendants in this century did not have a clue either, mistaking 'souatsche' for 'sou(r)atsche', thereby suggesting the box was of Japanese-Indian (Suratte) manufacture. Jhr. Dr. D.P.M. Graswinckel, *Graswinckel. Geschiedenis van een Delfts brouweres- en regenten-geslacht* (The Hague, 1956) 160-161.

17. ARA, records of the Nederlandse Factorij Japan: Inv. 327, letter dated Nagasaki 29 October 1696. Cornelis van Outhoorn (also spelled: Oudhoorn/ Outshoorn/ Oudshoorn) was the younger brother of Willem van Outhoorn (1635-1720), Governor-General from 1691-1704.
W. Wijnaendts van Resandt, *De gezaghebbers der Oost-Indische Compagnie op hare Buiten-Comptoiren in Azië* (Amsterdam, 1944)

18. Dr. J. Feenstra Kuiper, *Japan en de buitenwereld in de achttiende eeuw* (The Hague, 1921) 91-92.

19. ARA, records of the Nederlandse Factorij Japan: Inv. 880, Journal of Deshima, 15 October 1696

20. Ibidem, Inv. 328, letter dated 30 October 1696.

21. Ibid., Inv. 881

22. Ibid., Inv. 328

23. C.R. Boxer, *A true description of the mighty kingdoms of Japan & Siam by Caron & Schouten* (Amsterdam/ New York, 1971) 51.

24. A. Cleyer, *Tagebuch des Kontors zu Nagasaki auf der Insel Deshima 20. Oktober 1682 – 5.November 1683. Bearbeitet von Eva S. Kraft* (Bonn, 1985) p. 76: diary 17 December 1682.

25. E. Kaempfer, *Geschichte und beschreibung von Japan. Aus den Originalhandschriften des Verfassers herausgegeben von Christian Wilhelm Dohm. Unveränderter Neudruck des 1777-1779 im Verlag der Meyerschen Buchhandlung im Lemgo erschienen Originalwerks.* Vol. II (Stuttgart, 1964) 118.

26. E. Kaempfer, *De beschrijving van Japan. In 't Hoogduytsch beschreven door Engelbert Kaempfer Ö in het Engelsch overgeset, door J.G. Scheudzer Ö en uyt het Engelsch in 't Nederduytsch vertaalt* (Amsterdam, 1733) 483. There are several differences in the translated versions of the work. In the Dutch and English version *sowaas* and *sawaas* is mentioned four times, in the German version only once. The English translation happened to be the first publication. The English translator worked from the original manuscript and also had access to Kaempfers notes. The first German version was published in 1777, also from the original manuscript but apparently a shorter version.

27. Kaempfer, *Beschrijving van Japan,* 188. The Dutch translator seems to have added the word *sawaas* here.

28. G.E. Rumphius, *D'Amboinsche Rariteitkamer, behelzende eene beschrijving van allerhande zoo weeke als harde schaalvissen... alsmede allerhande hoorntjes en schulpen... benevens zommige mineraalen, gesteenten.* (Amsterdam, 1741) Book III, part IV, 202.

29. Victoria & Albert Museum, London, Inv. 200-1881, 168-1886.

30. Inventory Rüstkammer, Dresden. See category **A** in this catalogue. Also, according to the inventory, Elector August II added them, in portions, in 1704 and 1711 to the collection. Swords made in the same period are in the Hermitage, St. Petersburg (see fig. 11).

31. Rijksmuseum Amsterdam, Inv. NG-1978-99. See category **A** in this catalogue.

32. See category **D** in this catalogue.

33. Rijksmuseum Amsterdam, Department of Dutch History, object documentation system.

34. R. van Luttervelt, *Kunst in Nederland. Schilders van het stilleven* (Naarden, 1947), plate 30. The painting is private property. We have not been able to trace it. On the black and white photograph it is not visible whether these are silver or Sawasa objects. Van Roestraten worked in England most of his life.

35. F. Bonanni, *Verhandeling over de vernissen waarin de wyze opgegeeven wordt om er een toe te stellen dat 't Chineesch vernis volmaakt gelykt: Benevens verscheide andere zaken rakende de schilderkunst, 't vergulden, 't etsen etc.* J. Willeke (Leiden, 1742)
F. Bonanni, *Trattaro sopra La Vernice Detta*

communemente Cinese (Roma, 20 Martii 1720) Editrice Turris (Cremona, 1994)

36. Bonanni, *Verhandeling,* 65; Bonanni, *Trattaro,* 44 ('sciable', sciabolo=sword)

37. Bonanni, *Verhandeling,* 122-123

38. Ibidem, 166

39. Dr. C.J.A. Jörg, *Porcelain and the Dutch China trade* (The Hague, 1982) 93

40. Kaempfer, *Beschrijving van Japan,* 239

41. Ibidem, 264-265. Kaempfer witnessed the beheading of two Japanese smugglers in 1691. He says in seven years 700 were executed in Nagasaki.

42. Ibid., 264

43. Penelope Maskell, *Shakudo. A Japanese Art for the European Market* (Unpublished thesis). In the Deshima museum is a wooden small-sword.

44. Kaempfer, *Beschrijving van Japan,* 278

45. An example is a namban tsuba in the Rijksmuseum voor Volkenkunde Leiden, Inv. 3603-33. See also figure 6 in this catalogue.

46. Municipal Archives Amsterdam Inv. 5006., p. 735, inventory of the estate of Joan van Hoorn, Batavia 1711
Provincial Archives of Noord-Brabant, Nassause Domeinarchieven Inv. nr. 894, inventory of the estate of Gustaaf Willem Baron van Imhoff, Batavia November 9, 1750.

47. Rijksarchief Arnhem, archives Rosendael Inv. 781. Inventory of Willem van Outhoorn, December 1720. Kind communication of Ebeltje Hartkamp–Jonxis (Rijksmuseum Amsterdam).

48. Rijksmuseum Amsterdam, Inv. SK-A-3769. See figure 16 in this catalogue.

49. Hendrik Rennebaum, silversmith and member of the Lutheran Church Council, was declared insane in 1780. As a result of this, his wordly possessions, no doubt on the council's request, would be transferred to his family. He died in 1793. National Archives Jakarta, Inv. Fam. 513, 10 October 1780. Kind communication of S.M. Voskuil-Groenewegen and Willem Terlouw (Museum Princessehof Leeuwarden).

50. For the Dresden collection, see before and in this catalogue: Nos. A.6.1, A 8.1 and F.3.4. The Hermitage has a group of early Sawasa hangers and small-swords.

51. Å. Setterwall, *The Chinese Pavilion at Drottningholm* (Malmö, 1974) Catalogue FE 256.

52. For information on Sichterman, see: W. Kühne-van Diggelen, *Jan Albert Sichterman. VOC-dienaar en 'koning' van Groningen* (Groningen, 1995)

53. Rijksarchief Groningen, Archive Sichterman, No. 605-A. *Catalogus van een fraay Cabinet konstige en playsante Schilderijen etc.* [ ] J.A. Sichterman, [to be sold August 20 1764] (Groningen, 1764) 40-41. Kind communication of Jan van Campen (University of Leiden) and Christiaan Jörg (Groninger Museum).

54. Municipal archives Amsterdam, Inv. No. unknown, *Catalogue [ ] of [ ] many odd curiosities [ ] from the late Constant Sennepart, [to be sold] Amsterdam April 1, 1704.* Kind

communication of Jan van de Waals.

55. Municipal archives Amsterdam, Inv. No. unknown, *Catalogue [ ] of [ ] curiosities [ ] from the inheritance of the gentleman Mr Wouter Valckenier*. Kind communication of Jan van de Waals.

56. F. Lugt, *Répertoire des Catalogues de ventes publiques intéressant l'art ou la curiosité.* (The Hague, 1938-1987) (also called Lugt Repertorium) 368-2 (Card 18), *Catalogue of many Persian, Mongolian, Japanese [ ] coins, jewellery, [ ] and other curiosities from the Cabinet of the honourable gentleman Mr. Nicolaas Witzen, [to be sold starting from] March 30, 1728.* Kind communication of Ebeltje Hartkamp-Jonxis (Rijksmuseum Amsterdam)

57. Inventory Roelof Blok, streekarchief Hoorn, notariëel archief Enkhuizen, not. A. van der Willigen, Inv. 1390, July 10 1776. Cited in: Y.M. Prins: *Relaties, rijkdom en macht; Roelof Blok (1712-1776) een VOC-dienaar* (Unpublished masters thesis, Leiden, 1996). Kind communication of Ebeltje Hartkamp-Jonxis (Rijksmuseum Amsterdam)

58. Lugt Repertorium 5672, *Catalogue of [ ] precious curiosities such as Tonquinese chiselled, porcelain [ ] of the late [ ] Pieter Cornelis Hasselaar [announced in the Amsterdam Newspaper], November 18, 1797.*

59. J. van Campen, 'De verzameling van de amateur-sinioloog J.Th. Royer in het Rijksmuseum', in: *Bulletin van het Rijksmuseum* 43 1 (Amsterdam, 1995) 3-35.

60. Item No. 216. The original inventory is in the Museum voor Volkenkunde Leiden. A copy is at the Department of B&K in the Rijksmuseum Amsterdam.

61. R.P. van de Kasteele, *Handleiding voor de bezichtiging van het kabinet van zeldzaamheden* (The Hague, 1824) 26. In the nineteenth century this collection was divided among several Dutch museums. Some of these objects were traded for other artefacts with a jeweller, c. 1920. There is a possibility some of these objects are or have been at the Museum voor Volkenkunde in Leiden.

62. W.J.M. Buch, *De Oost-Indische Compagnie en Quinam. De betrekkingen der Nederlanders met Annam in de XVIIe eeuw.* Doctoral Thesis (Amsterdam, 1921)

63. J.B. du Halde, *Description [etc.] de l'empire de la Chine* (The Hague, 1736) 4 Vols. Vol II, p. 209.

64. H. Yude and A.C. Burnell, *Hobson-Jobson. The Anglo-Indian Dictionary.* First published 1886. (London, 1996) Tutenag became fashionable in Europe in the eighteenth century. A. Bonin, *Tutenag and paktong* (Oxford, 1925)

65. Halde, *Description [etc] de l'empire de la Chine*, Vol 1, 207.

66. P. Osbeck, *Reise nach Ostindien und China* (Rostock, 1765) 131-203.

67. Friendly communication by Mr. Takatoshi Misugi who reminded us of the fact that craftsmen generally circulated among the top workshops in Kyoto and other cities, such as Nagasaki.

68. For instance several Straits Chinese Silver objects ressemble Sawasa wares in shape and decoration. Ho Wing Meng, *Straits Chinese Silver: a collectors guide*, (Singapore, 1984). Kind communication of mr. W.E. Bouwman, Aalderink Antiques.

Chapter 3

1. R. Murakami, S. Niiyama and M. Kitada, *Characterization of the Black Surface Layer on a Copper Alloy coloured by Traditional Japanese Surface Treatment.* (Kyoto, 1988) 133-136

2. J. Kumanotani e.a., 'Attempts to understand Japanese Lacquer as a Super Durable Material', in: Yoshimichi Emoto and Hisao Mabuchi (eds.), *International Symposium on the Conservation and Restoration of Cultural Property* (Kyoto, 1978) 51-63

3. M. Derrick, C. Druzik, F. Preusser, 'FTIR Analysis of Authentic and Simulated Black Laquer Finishes on Eighteen Century Furniture', *Urushi. Proceedings of the Urushi Study Group, June, 10-27 1985.* Tokyo. (Maria del Rey, 1988) 163-189

Chapter 4

1. For example, the famous *chine de commande*, described by Dr. C.J.A. Jörg in: *Chinese Export Porcelain. Chine de Commande from the Royal Museums of Art and History in Brussels* (Hong Kong 1989) Exhibition catalogue

2. See about metal export wares: H.A. Forbes e.a., *Chinese Export Silver. 1785 to 1885* (Milton/Massachusetts, 1975)

3. The symbolical meanings described in this chapter are based on: W. Eberhart, *A Dictionary of Chinese Symbols. Hidden Symbols in Chinese Life and Thought.* (London/New York, 1986), H.L. Joly, *Legend in Japanese Art. A Description of Historical Episodes, Legendary Characters, Folk-lore, Myths, Religious Symbolism, Illustrated in the Arts of Old Japan.* (Rutland, 1973) and C.L. van der Pijl-Ketel, *The Ceramic Load of the 'Witte Leeuw'. 1613* (Amsterdam, 1982) Exhibition catalogue Rijksmuseum Amsterdam

4. See, for example, J. Rawson, *Chinese Ornament. The Lotus and the Dragon.* (New York, 1984)

5. K.M. Ball, *Decorative Motives of Oriental Art* (London 1927) 164.

6. In Tonkinese art, the squirrel, or an animal that very strongly resembled a squirrel, was usually combined with clusters of nuts, called *caӯ cô giàc* in Vietnamese, instead of grape vines.

Bibliography

ARA = Algemeen Rijks Archief, the Hague

History

Babbitt, F.C., *Plutarch: Moralia* (London, 1936)

Baron, S., *A Voyage to Cochinchina in the Years 1792-93* (Londen, 1805)

Berthelot, M., *La Chimie au Moyen Age*, I-III (Paris, 1893)

Bierens de Haan, J.C., *Rosendael, Groen Hemeltjen op Aerd. Kasteel, tuinen en bewoners sedert 1579* (Zutphen, 1994)

Boardman, J., 'Silver is White', *Revue Archeologique*, **2** (Paris, 1987) 279-85.

Bonanni, F., *Verhandeling over de vernissen waarin de wyze opgegeeven wordt om er een toe te stellen dat 't Chineesch vernis volmaakt gelykt: Benevens verscheyde andere zaken rakende de schilderkunst, 't vergulden, 't etsen etc*, Jacobus Willeke (Leiden, 1742)

Bonanni, F., *Trattatro sopra La Vernice Detta communemente Cinese* (Roma, 20 Martii 1720) Editrice Turris (Cremona, 1994)

Bonnin, A., *Tutenay and Paktong* (Oxford, 1924)

Boudet, P. and A. Masson, *Iconographie historique de l'Indochine* (Paris, 1933)

Boxer, C.R., *A True Description of the Mighty Kingdoms of Japan & Siam by Caron & Schouten* (Amsterdam/ New York, 1971)

Boxer, C.R., *Jan Compagnie in Japan 1600-1817* (The Hague, 1950)

Buch, W.J.M., *De Oost-Indische Compagnie en Quinam. De betrekkingen der Nederlanders met Annam in de XVIIe eeuw*, Doctoral Thesis (Amsterdam, 1921)

Canavarro, P. e.a. *Art Namban. Les Portugais au Japon/ Nambankunst. Portugezen in Japan* (Brussels, 1989) Exhibition catalogue Koninklijke Musea voor Kunst en Geschiedenis

Cardin, P.F., *Relations de ce qui c'est passé depuis quelques années jusques . l'an 1644 du Japon à la Cochinchine* (Paris, 1646)

Casal, U.A., 'Japanese Art Lacquers', *Monumenta Nipponica. Studies on Japanese Culture. Past and Present*, **15** Nos. 1-4 (Tokyo, 1959/60)

Chase, W.T. and U.M. Franklin, 'Early Chinese Black Mirrors and Pattern-etched Weapons', *Ars Orientalis*, **11** (Ann Arbor, 1979) 215-58

Conner, P., *The China Trade. 1600-1860* (Edinburgh, 1982) Exhibition catalogue The Royal Pavilion Art Gallery and Museums, Brighton

Chijs, mr. J. A. van der, *Nederlandsch Indisch Plakaatboek, 1602-1811*, Part 10: *1776-1787* (Batavia, 1892)

Cleyer, A., *Tagebuch des Kontors zu Nagasaki auf der Insel Deshima 20. Oktober 1682 – 5.November 1683*. Bearbeited von Eva S. Kraft (Bonn, 1985)

Coolhaas, W.Ph. and J. van Goor (eds.), *Generale Missieven van Gouverneurs-Generaal en Raden aan Heren XVII der Verenigde Oostindische Compagnie*, Part II: *1639-1655* (The Hague, 1960) Rijks Geschiedkundige Publicatiën 112

Coolhaas, W.Ph. and J. van Goor (eds.), *Generale Missieven van Gouverneurs-Generaal en Raden aan Heren XVII der Verenigde Oostindische Compagnie* Part III: *1655-1674* (The Hague, 1960) Rijks Geschiedkundige Publicatiën 125

Cooney, J.D., 'On the Meaning of Hsmn Km', *Zeitschrift für Ägyptische Sprache und Altertumskunde*, **93** (Berlin, 1966) 43-7

Cooney, J.D., 'Siren and Ba: Birds of a Feather', *Bulletin of the Cleveland Museum*, **55** (Cleveland, 1968) 262-71

Croix, A. de la, *Relations de la nouvelle mission des pères de la Compagnie de Iezus au Rouyaume de la Cochinchine* (Lille, 1631)

Dube, R.K., 'Some Literary and Documentary Evidences for Coloured Gold in Ancient India', *Bulletin of the Metals Museum of the Japan Institute of Metals*, **26** 2 (1996) 27-32

Dumoutier, 'L'Indochine et ses Anciennes Relations commercials avec le Japon', *Revue française du Japon*, **1** (Tokyo, 1892)

Ee, K.J., *The Straits Chinese. A Cultural History* (Amsterdam/Singapore, 1996)

Feenstra Kuiper, Dr. J., *Japan en de buitenwereld in de achttiende eeuw* (The Hague, 1921)

French, C., *Through closed doors: Western Influence on Japanese Art. 1639-1853* (Rochester, 1977) Exhibition catalogue Meadow Brook Art Gallery and the University of Michigan Museum of Art

Gawronski, J. e.a., *Hollandia Compendium. A contribution to the history, archeology, classification and lexicography of a 150 ft. Dutch East Indiaman (1740-1750)* (Amsterdam, 1992)

Gentle, R. and R. Feild, *Domestic Metalwork. 1640-1820* (Woodbridge, 1994)

Giumlia Mair, A.R., 'Das Krokodil und Amenemhat III aus el-Faiyum', *Antike Welt. Zeitschrift für Archäologie und Kulturgeschichte*, 1996 4 (Feldmeilen, 1996) 313-22

Giumlia Mair, A.R., 'Das Sichelschwert von Bâlata-Sichem', *Antike Welt. Zeitschrift für Archäologie und Kulturgeschichte*, 1996 4 (Feldmeilen, 1996) 340

Giumlia Mair, A.R. and P.T. Craddock, 'Corinthium Aes: das schwarze Gold der Alchimisten', *Antike Welt. Zeitschrift für Archäologie und Kulturgeschichte*, Sondernummer **23** (Mainz am Rhein, 1993)

Giumlia Mair, A.R. and S. Quirke, 'Black Copper in Bronze Age Egypt', *Revue d'Egyptologie* **48** (Paris, 1997) 95-108.

Goldstein, J., 'The Metallurgy of the Meiji Period', *Arts of Asia*, **27** August (4) (Hong Kong, 1997) 76-78

Graaff, S. de and D.G. Stibbe (eds.), *Encyclopaedie van Nederlandsch-Indië* (The Hague/Leiden, 1917-1939)

Graswinckel, Jhr. Dr. D.P.M., *Graswinckel: geschiedenis van een Delfts Brouwers- en Regenten-geslacht* (The Hague, 1956)

Halde, J.B. du, *Description [etc] de l'Empire de la Chine*, Vol. 1 & II (The Hague, 1736)

Kasteele, R.P. van de, *Handleiding voor de Bezichtiging van het Kabinet der Zeldzaamheden* (The Hague, 1824) Collection catalogue of the Koninklijke Kabinet der Zeldzaamheden

Hayward, J.F., 'Rare Items in Shakudo: from a collector', *The Times*, 30-01-1960 (London, 1960)

Herberts, Dr. K., *Das Buch der Ostasiatischen Lackkunst* (Dusseldorf, 1959)

Herdtle, *Ostasiatische Bronce- gefässe und geräte*, Vol. II (Vienna, 1883) 649

Huard, P. and M. Durand, *Viet-Nam, Civilization and Culture* (Paris, 1994)

Howard, D.S., *A Tale of three Cities. Canton, Shanghai & Hong Kong. Three Centuries of Sino-British Trade in the Decorative Arts* (London, 1997) Exhibition catalogue Sotheby's.

Huyser, Mr. J.G., 'Oud-Javaansche Koper-Legeeringen', *Cultureel Indië*, **1** Part I, II, III (Leiden, 1939)

Croissant, D. and L. Ledderose (eds.). *Japan und Europa, 1543-1929* (Berlin, 1993) Exhibition catalogue on the occasion of the 43rd Berliner Festspiele.

Jasper, J.E. and Mas Pirngadie, *De Inlandsche Kunstnijverheid in Nederlandsch Indië*, Part IV: *De Goud en Zilversmeedkunst* (The Hague, 1927)

Jasper, J.E. and Mas Pirngadie, *De Inlandsche Kunstnijverheid in Nederlandsch Indië*, Part V: *De Bewerking van Niet-Edele Metalen (koperbewerking en pamorsmeedkunst)* (The Hague, 1930)

Joly, H.L., *Legend in Japanese Art. A Description of Historical Episodes, Legendary Characters, Folk-lore, Myths, Religious Symbolism, Illustrated in the Arts of Old Japan* (Rutland, 1973)

Jones, H.L., *Pausanias: Description of Greece* (London, 1918)

Jones, M. (ed.), *Why Fakes Matter* (London, 1992).

Jörg, C.J.A., *Porcelain and the Dutch China trade* (The Hague, 1982)

Jourdain, M. and R. Soame Jenyns, *Chinese Export Art in the eighteenth century* (London/New York, 1950)

Kaempfer, E., *The History of Japan*, Vol. I (London, 1727)

Kaempfer, E., *De Beschrijving van Japan*, Vol. IV (Amsterdam, 1733)

Kaempfer, E., *Geschichte und Beschreibung von Japan: aus den Originalhandschriften des Verfassers herausgegeben von Christian Wilhelm Dohm. Unveränderter Neudruck des 1777-1779 im Verlag der Meyerschen Buchhandlung im Lemgo erschienen Originalwerks*, Part II (Stuttgart, 1964)

Kist, J.B., 'Shakudo/Suassa. Een tentoonstelling in de afdeling Nederlandse Geschiedenis van het Rijksmuseum, Amsterdam', *Aziatische Kunst*, **28** (1) (Amsterdam, 1998) 28-34

Koffler, J., 'Description historique de la Cochinchine', *Revue Indochinoise*, XV (Paris, 1911)

Kühne-van Diggelen, W., *Jan Albert Sichterman. VOC-dienaar en 'koning' van Groningen* (Groningen, 1995)

Kümmel, O., *Kunstgewerbe in Japan* (Berlin, 1901)

La Niece S., 'Japanese Polychrome Metalwork', *Archaeometry '90* (Basel, 1990) 87-94.

La Niece, S. and P.T. Craddock, *Metal Plating and Patination* (Oxford,1993)

Lee, J.L., *Philadelphians and the China Trade, 1784-1735* (Philadelphia, 1984) Exhibition catalogue Philadelphia Museum of Art

Lubberhuizen–van Gelder, A.M., 'De factorijen te Canton in de 18e eeuw', *Oud-Holland. Driemaandelijks Tijdschrift voor Nederlandse Kunstgeschiedenis*, I-IV (Amsterdam, 1955)

Lugt, F., *Répertoire des Catalogues de ventes publiques intéressant l'art ou la curiosité* (The Hague, 1938-1987)

Medhurst, W.H., *An English and Japanese and Japanese and English Vocabulary: compiled from Native Works* (Batavia, 1830)

Meilingk-Roelofsz. M.A.P. e.a., *De archieven van de Verenigde Oostindische Compagnie/The archives of the*

Dutch East India Company (1602-1795), ARA, Eerste Afdeling (The Hague, 1992)

Needham, J., *Science and Civilisation in China*, **5** (2) (Cambridge, 1974) 257-71.

Newman, H., *An Illustrated Dictionary of Silverware: 2,373 entries, relating to British and North American wares, decorative techniques and styles, and leading designers and makers, principally from c.1500 to the present* (London, 1987)

Nihon daijiten kankokai (ed.), *Nihon kokugo daijiten*, Vol. 9 (Tokyo, 1976) Japanese dictionary

Oddy, W.A. and W. Zwalf, 'Aspects of Tibetan Metalwork', *British Museum Occasional Paper*, **15** (London, 1981) 33-67

Osbeck P., *Reise nach Ostindien und China* (Rostock, 1765)

Overmeer Fisscher, J.F. van, *Bijdrage tot de kennis van het Japansche rijk* (Amsterdam. 1833)

Ovington, Rev. F., *A Voyage to Surrat in the Year 1689* (London, 1696)

Pijl-Ketel, C.L. van der, *The Ceramic Load of the 'Witte Leeuw'. 1613* (Amsterdam, 1982) Exhibition catalogue Rijksmuseum Amsterdam

Raay, S. van (ed.), *Imitation and Inspiration. Japanese Influence on Dutch Art* (Amsterdam, 1989)

Rackham, H., *Pliny: The Natural History* III (London, 1940)

Rackham, H., *Pliny: The Natural History* IX (London, 1952)

Râ[y, A.C., *History of Chemistry in Ancient and Medieval India* (Calcutta, 1956)

Rein, J.J., 'Japan nach Reisen und Studien', Vol. II: *Land- und Forstwirthschaft, Industrie und Handel* (Leipzig, 1886)

Remius, I., *Journal Hållen på resan till Canton 1745-1748*, Birgit Lumelund (ed.), Svenska Litteratursällskapet i Finland CCLXXIII (Helsinki, 1939)

Roessingh, M.P.H., 'Een japon de commande lakdoos', in: *Verslagen en Aanwinsten 80-81. Cultuurgeschiedenis Nederlanders Overzee* (Amsterdam, 1981)

Rumphius, G.E., *D'Amboinsche Rariteitkamer, behelzende eene beschrijving van allerhande zoo weeke als harde schaalvissen... alsmede allerhande hoorntjes an schulpen... benevens zommige mineraalen, gesteenten* (Amsterdam, 1741)

Saur, K.G. 'Multilingual Glossary for Art Librarians. English with Indexes in Dutch, French, German, Italian, Spanish and Swedish', *IFLA Publications 75* (München/New Providence/London and Paris, 1996)

Siebold, P.F., *Nippon. Archiv zur Beschreibung von Japan und dessen Neben- und Schutzländern, jezo mit*

den Südlichen Kurilen, Sachalin, Korea und den Liukiu-Inseln, Vol. I (Würzburg/Leipzig, 1897)

Sperlich, M., e.a., *China und Europa. Chinaverständnis und Chinamode im 17. und 18. Jahrhundert* (Berlin, 1973) Exhibition catalogue Schloß Charlottenburg, Berlin

Stapleton, C. e.a., '*Corinthium Aes* and Black Bronze in the Early Medieval Period', *Antiquaries Journal* **75** (London, 1995) 383-90

Stillwell, R. e.a., 'Corinth', **1** 2, *Architecture* (Cambridge, Mass., 1941)

Thiel, P.J.J. van, *All the paintings of the Rijksmuseum on Amsterdam: a completely illustrated catalogue* (Maarssen, 1976) Museum catalogue Rijksmuseum Amsterdam. Department of Paintings

Upmark, G., *Nordiska Museet Samlingar. Bilder och Tillägnade* (Stockholm, 1925) Museum catalogue of the Nordiska Museet in Stockholm

Vickers, M., 'Artful Crafts: the Influence of Metalwork on Athenian Painted Pottery', *Journal of Hellenic Studies*, **105** (London, 1985) 108-28.

Voskuil-Groenewegen, S.M., *V.O.C.-zilver. Zilver uit de periode van de Verenigde Oostindische Compagnie. 17e en 18e eeuw* (The Hague, 1983) Museum catalogue Haags Gemeentemuseum

Wagenaar, L. e.a., *De wereld binnen handbereik. De Nederlandse kunst- en rariteitenverzamelingen, 1585-1735* (Amsterdam, 1992) Museum catalogue Amsterdams Historisch Museum

Wijnaendts van Resandt, W., *De gezaghebbers der Oost-Indische Compagnie op hare Buiten-Comptoiren in Azië* (Amsterdam, 1944)

Yude, H. and A.C. Burnell, *Hobson-Jobson: The Anglo-Indian Dictionary*, First published 1886. (London, 1996)

Zedler, *Universal Lexicon*, Vol.36 (1742)

Asian Art

Armstrong, N., *Fans: A Collector's Guide* (London, 1984)

Ayers, J. e.a., *Porcelain for Palaces. The fashion for Japan in Europe. 1650-1750* (London, 1990) Exhibition catalogue British Museum

The Beauty of Black and Gold Japanese Lacquer: Makie (Kyoto 1995) Exhibition catalogue Kyoto National Museum

Bernanose, M., *Les arts décoratifs au Tonkin* (Paris, 1922)

Boyer, M., *Japanese Export Lacquers from the seventeenth century in the National Museum of Denmark* (Copenhagen, 1959) Museum catalogue National Museum.

Crossman, C.L., *A Catalogue of Chinese Trade Paintings, Furniture, Silver and other Objects. 1785-*

1865 (Salem, 1970) Museum catalogue Peabody Museum

Clunas, C., *Chinese Export and Design* (Westerham, 1978) Museum catalogue Victoria & Albert Museum

Clunas, C., *Chinese Export Watercolours* (London, 1984)

Fans from the East (London, 1978) Exhibition catalogue Birmingham City and Art Gallery

Feddersen, M., *Chinese Decorative Art: a handbook for collectors and connoisseurs* (London, 1961)

Feddersen, M., *Japanese Decorative Art: a handbook for collectors and connoisseurs* (London, 1962)

Fine Chinese Ceramics, Paintings, Jades, Works of Art and Export Porcelain (London, 1997) Auction catalogue Christies

Fine Chinese Ceramics, Paintings, Jades, Works of Art and Export Porcelain (London, 1998) Auction catalogue Christies

Forbes, H.A., e.a., *Chinese Export Silver: 1785 to 1885* (Milton (Mass.), 1975) Museum catalogue Museum of the American China Trade

Gabbert, G., *Ostasiatische Lackkunst* (Frankfurt a/Main, 1978) Exhibition catalogue Museum f﹐r Kunsthandwerk, Frankfurt am Main

Hawthorn, G. e.a., *Oriental Works of Art* (London, 1992) Sales catalogue of The Oriental Art Gallery Ltd.

Hawthorn, G. e.a., *Oriental Works of Art* (London, 1994) Sales catalogue of The Oriental Art Gallery Ltd.

Hawthorn, G. e.a., *Oriental Works of Art* (London, 1995) Sales catalogue of The Oriental Art Gallery Ltd.

Hawthorn, G. (ed.), *Oriental Works of Art* (London, 1997) Sales catalogue of Gerard Hawthorn Oriental Art Gallery Ltd.

Iröns, N.J., 'Silver & Carving of the Old China Trade', *Oriental Art Series*, Nos. 3 & 4 (London/Hong Kong, 1983)

Janssens, B. e.a., *Oriental Jewellery and Works of Art* (London, 1993) Sales catalogue of the Oriental Art Gallery Ltd.

Janssens, B. e.a., *Oriental Jewellery and Works of Art* (London, 1994) Sales catalogue of the Oriental Art Gallery Ltd.

Japanese Works of Art (London, 1998) Auction catalogue Sotheby's

Jörg, dr. C.J.A., *Chinese Export Porcelain: Chine de Commande from the Royal Museums of Art and History in Brussels* (Hong Kong, 1989) Exhibition catalogue Royal Museums of Art and History

Kakudo, Y., *Later Japanese Lacquers* (San Francisco, 1987) Publication for the exhibition with the same title in the Asian Art Museum of San Francisco

Kao, M., *Chinese Ivories from the Kwan Collection* (Hong Kong, 1990) Exhibition catalogue Art Gallerie, Chinese University of Hong Kong

Kerr, R., *Later Chinese Bronzes* (London, 1990)

Kopplin, M., *Ostasiatische Lackkunst: ausgewählte Arbeiten* (Lengerich, 1993) Museum catalogue Museum für Lackkunst München.

Ling Roth, H., *Oriental Silverwork. Malay and Chinese: A Handbook for Connoisseurs, Collectors, Students and Silversmiths* (Kuala Lumpur, 1966)

Meng, Ho Wing, *Straits Chinese Silver: A Collector's Guide* (Singapore, 1984)

Mowry, R.D., *China's Renaissance in Bronze. The Robert H. Clague Collection of Later Chinese Bronzes. 1100-1900* (Phoenix, 1993) Exhibition catalogue Phoenix Art Museum

Pekarik, A.J., *Japanese Lacquer. 1600-1900: Selections from the Charles A. Greenfield Collection* (New York, 1980) Exhibition catalogue Metropolitan Museum of Art

Setterwall, Ä. e.a., *The Chinese Pavilion at Drottningholm* (Malmö, 1974) Collection catalogue Drottningholm

Strange, E.F., *Catalogue of Chinese Lacquer* (London, 1970) Museum catalogue Victoria & Albert Museum, Department of Woodwork

Weinmayr, E., *Nurimono. Japanische Lackmeister der Gegenwart* (München, 1996) Exhibition catalogue Museum für Lackkunst

White, J.M. e.a., *Adornment for Eternity: Status and Rank in Chinese Ornament* (Denver, 1994) Exhibition catalogue Denver Art Museum.

Wiedhage, P., *Goldene Gründe. Japanische Lackarbeiten in Museum für Kunst und Gewerbe, Hamburg* (Hamburg, 1996) Exhibition catalogue Museum für Kunst und Gewerbe

Technology

Benninghoff, H., 'Mechanische, chemische und elektrolytische Oberflächenvorbehandlung von Kupfer und Kupferlegierungen. Ein Literaturbericht zu jüngsten Fortschritten', *DKI Sonderdruck* No. s. 152 (Berlin)

Boerhaave Beekman, W., 'Bossen, bomen en toegepast hout uit het verleden. Historie van de Grieken tot en met de Byzantijnen, bijzondere toepassingen tot het einde der 19e eeuw', in: *Hout in alle Tijden*, Part II (Deventer, 1949-1955)

Collier, H.B., 'Black Copper of Yunnan', *Journal of Chemical Education* **17** (Easton, 1940) 19-21

Collier, H.B., 'X-ray Fluorescence Analysis of Black Copper of Yunnan', *Natuurwissenschaften* **64** (1977) 484

Craddock, P.T., 'The Ancestors of Japanese *Irogane*', in: *Proceedings of the Forum for BUMA-IV* (Sendai,1996) 79-84

Craddock, P.T. and A. Giumlia Mair, 'The Identity of Corinthian Bronze: Rome's *Shakudo* Alloy, in: Mols, S.T.A.M. (ed.) e.a., *Acta of the 12th International Congress on Ancient Bronzes* (Nijmegen, 1995) 137-48

Demakopoulou, K. e.a., 'Mycenaean Black Inlaid Metalware in the National Archaeological Museum, Athens: A Technical Examination', *Annual of the British School at Athens*, **90** (Athens, 1995) 137-53

Derrick, M. e.a., 'FTIR Analysis of Authentic and Simulated Black Lacquer Finishes on Eighteen Century Furniture', *Urushi. Proceedings of the Urushi Study Group, June 10-27 1985, Tokyo* (Maria del Rey, 1988) 163-189

Giumlia Mair, A., 'Early Instances of *Shakudo*-type Alloys in the West', *Bulletin of the Metals Museum of the Japan Institute of Metals*, **27** (1997) 3-16

Giumlia Mair, A. and M. Lehr, 'Patinating Black Bronzes: texts and tests', in: *Proceedings of the BUMA IV Conference* (Matsue, 1998)

Gowland, W., 'A Japanese pseudo-speiss, (shirome)', *Journal of the Society of Chemical Industry*, **13** 5 (Tokyo, 1894) 1-26.

Haselbach, M., 'Dekorativer Innenausbau mit Kupfer und Kupferlegierungen', *DKI Sonderdruck*, No. s. 153 (Berlin)

Kleinau, M. and H.J. Lange, 'Emaillieren von Kupfer und Tombak', *DKI Sonderdruck*, No. s. 163 (Berlin)

Kumanotani, J. e.a., 'Attempts to understand Japanese Lacquer as a Super Durable Material', in: Yoshimichi Emoto and Hisao Mabuchi (eds.), *International Symposium on the Conservation and Restoration of Cultural Property* (Kyoto, 1978)

La Niece, S. and P.T. Craddock, *Metal Plating and Patination: Cultural, Technical and Historical Developments* (Oxford, 1993)

Lorac-Gerbaud, A., *Les Secrets du lacque. Techniques et histoire* (Paris, 1996)

Mang Zidan and Han Rubin, 'Studies of the Blackening on Copper-silver-gold Alloy', *Studies in the History of Natural Sciences*, **6** (4) (1989)

Michaels, A., *The Making of a Statue. Lost-Wax Casting in Nepal* (Stuttgart, 1988)

Milam, B. and H. Gillette, 'X-ray Radiography in the Study of Oriental Lacquerware Substructures', *Urushi. Proceedings of the Urushi Study Group. June 10-27, 1985. Tokyo* (Maria del Rey, 1988) 199-226

Murakami, R. e.a., *Characterization of the Black Surface Layer on a Copper Alloy coloured by Traditional Japanese Surface Treatment* (Kyoto, 1988)

Notis, M.R., 'The Japanese Alloy Shakudo: The History and its Patination', in: Maddin, R., *The Beginning of the use of Metals and Alloys* (Massachusetts, 1988)

Riederer, J., *Archeologie und Chemie* (Berlin 1987)

Roberts-Austen, W.C., *Report on the Analysis of Various Examples of Oriental Metalwork in the South Kensington Museum* (London, 1892)

Zao Gui-Fang and Hu Zheng-Hai, 'Ultrastructure of the Secretory Cell of Laticiferous Canals of *Rhus verniciflua* at Different Developmental Stages', *Chinese Journal-of Botany*, 1 (1) (Bejing, 1989) 49

Zhao, X. Q., 'A Method of Isolating Lacquer Ducts from Bark of Lacquer Trees (Anacardiaceae: Rhus Verniciflua Stokes) with Snail (Mollusca: Ahatinidae: Achatina Fulica Fer.) Digestive Juice', *Wuyi Science Journal*, 6 (Bejing, 1986) 328

Decorations

Bartholomew, T.T., *Myths and Rebuses in Chinese Art* (San Fransisco, 1988) Publication for the exhibition with the same title at the Asian Art Museum of San Francisco

Crossman, C.L., *The Decorative Arts of The China Trade. Paintings, Furnishings and Exotic Curiosities* (Woodbridge, 1991)

Eberhart, W., *A Dictionary of Chinese Symbols. Hidden Symbols in Chinese Life and Thought* (London/New York, 1986)

Jansen, E.R. (ed.), *Het Boeddha-boekje. Boeddha's, godheden and rituele symbolen* (Diever, 1990)

Joly, H.L., *Legend in Japanese Art. A Description of Historical Episodes, Legendary Characters, Folk-lore, Myths, Religious Symbolism, Illustrated in the Arts of Old Japan* (Rutland, 1973)

Lee, S.E., *Japanese Decorative Style* (New York, 1961) Introduction to the catalogue of the exhibition at The Cleveland Museum of Art

Misugi, T., *Chinese Porcelain Collections in the Near East. Topkapi and Ardebil*, Vol. I (Hong Kong, 1981)

Rawson, J., *Chinese Ornament. The Lotus and the Dragon* (New York, 1984)

Schwarz, K.M., *Netsuke Subjects. A Study on the Netsuke Themes with References to their Interpretation and Symbolism* (Vienna, 1992)

Volker, T., *The Animal in the Far Eastern Art and especially in the Art of the Japanese Netsuke with references to Chinese Origins, Traditions, Legends and Art* (Leiden, 1975)

Arms

Angel, J.C., *De Samurai. Japanse krijgsheren, hun zwaarden en zwaardsieraden* (Hapert, 1983) Exhibition catalogue Rijksmuseum voor Volkenkunde

Bashford Dean, *Catalogue of European Daggers. Including the Ellis, De Dino, Riggs and Reubell Collections* (New York, 1929) Museum catalogue Metropolitan Museum of Art

Bashford Dean, *Catalogue of European Court Swords and Hunting Swords* (New York, 1929) Museum catalogue Metropolitan Museum of Art

Bashford Dean, 'The Reubell Collection of Court Swords and Early Daggers', *Bulletin of the Metropolitan Museum of Art*, Vol. XXI, No. 10 (New York, 1926)

Brinkley, Captain F., 'Japan: its history, arts and literature', Vol. VIII: *Pictorial and Applied Art* (Boston/Tokyo, 1902)

Cederström, R., 'Japanska Värjfästen i Europeiska 1700-talsformer', in: Upmark, G., *Nordiska Museet Samlingar. Bilder och Tillägnade* (Stockholm, 1925) Museum catalogue of the Nordiska Museet in Stockholm

Haenel, E., *Kostbare Waffen aus der Dresdener Rüstkammer* (Leipzig, 1923)

Hartmans, C.A., *Nederlandse Zwaardvegers - mimeographed edition-* (Breda, 1965)

Jaarverslag 1963. Nederlands Leger- en Wapenmuseum 'Generaal Hoefer' (Leiden, 1964)

Milward, C., 'European Decoration on Japanese Sword Guards', Part II, *The Antique Collector*, April 1967 (London, 1967) 74-77

Milward, C., 'Japanes Sword Guards. Some Examples of European Decoration', Part I, *The Antique Collector*, October 1996 (London, 1996) 204-208

Norman, A.V.B. and C.M. Barne, *The rapier and the small sword 1460-1820* (London, 1980)

Opis: Opis Moskovskoy Oruzheynoy Palaty (Moscow, 1885) Inventory Kremlin Armoury

Puijpe, J.P., *Blanke wapens: Nederlandse slag- en steekwapens sinds 1600: zwaarden, degens, sabels en ponjaards: historisch overzicht en typologie* (Lochem-Poperinge, 1981)

Puijpe, J.P., *The Visser Collection. Arms of the Netherlands in the collection of H.L. Visser*, Part 3 (Zwolle, 1996) Collection catalogue

Robinson, B.W., *The Bauer Collection. Japanes Sword-fittings and associated metalwork* (Geneva, 1980) Collection catalogue

Seitz, H., *Blankwaffen II: Geschichte und Typenentwicklung im europäischen Kulturbereich vom 16. bis 19. Jahrhundert* (Braunschweig, 1968)

Tobacco and other stimulants

Claessens-Peré, A.–M. and L. de Ren, *Dozen om the niezen. Belgische en Franse snuifdozen en tabaksraspen uit de 18e eeuw* (Antwerpen, 1996) Exhibition catalogue Provinciaal Museum Sterckhof–Zilvercentrum

Duco, D.H., *De Nederlandse Kleipijp. Handboek voor Dateren en Determineren* (Leiden, 1987)

Gemar-Koeltzsch, E., *Luca Bild-Lexikon. Holländische Stillebenmaler im 17. Jahrhundert*, Vol. 3, L-Z (Lingen, 1994) 826-831

Leeuwrik, J.H.J., 'Koloniale Pijpfoudralen', *Antiek. Tijdschrift voor liefhebbers en kenners van oude kunst en kunstnijverheid*, 27 10 (Lochem, 1993) 481-485

Lunsingh Scheurleer, P., 'Nog eens een tabaks doosje uit Sumatra', *Mededelingenblad Vereniging van Vrienden der Aziatische Kunst Amsterdam*, 13 1 (Amsterdam, 1983)

Lutterveld, dr. R. van, *Kunst van Nederland. Schilders van het Stilleven* (Naarden, 1947)

Meijer, F. G., *Stillevens uit de Gouden Eeuw* (Rotterdam, 1989)

Shaw, L. B., 'Pieter van Roestraeten and the English Vanitas', *Burlington Magazine*, June 1990 (London, 1990)

Valentijn, F., *Oud en Nieuw Oost-Indië*, IV, Part II, in: Oyen, L.A.T.J.F. van, 'Bijdragen tot de kennis van sirih', *Bulletin Koloniaal Museum Haarlem*, 32 (Haarlem, 1904/05) 118-119

Wttewaal, B. W. G., *Klein Nederlands Zilver. 1650-1880* (Amsterdam, 1987)

Beverages

Adriaensens, A.-M., *Driemaal exotisch drinken. Cacoa, thee en koffie* (Antwerpen, 1993) Educational publication for the exhibition at the Museum Sterckhof-Zilvercentrum

Arnol, Dr. K.-P. e.a., 'Ey! Wie schmeckt der Coffee süße'. *Meissener Porzellan und Graphik* (Dresden, 1991) Exhibition catalogue Staatliche Kunstsammlungen Dresden

Emmerson, R., *British Teapots & Tea Drinking* (London, 1992) Collection catalogue Twining Teapot Gallery and Norwich Castle Museum

Kist, J.B., 'Een merkwaardig kofieservies', in: *Jaarverslagen 1974 en 1975 van de Stichting Cultuurgeschiedenis Nederlanders Overzee* (Amsterdam, 1976)

Kleyn, J. de, 'De kraantjeskan met conische vorm, een oud type koffiekan', *Antiek, Tijdschrift voor liefhebbers van oude kunst en kunstnijverheid*, No. 6, 1972 (Lochem, 1972) 433-445

Brown, P.B., *In Praise of Hot Liquors. The Study of Chocolate, Coffee and Tea-drinking. 1600-1850* (York, 1995) Exhibition catalogue Fairfax House, York

Reinders, P. e.a., *Koffie in Nederland. Vier eeuwen cultuurgeschiedenis* (Zutphen, 1994)

Clothing and accessories

Gandouet, T., *Boutons* (Paris, 1984)

Photo credits